An Early Start to Energy and its Effects

Roy Richards

SIMON & SCHUSTER
EDUCATION

Text © Roy Richards 1992
Artwork © Anna Hancock 1992

First Published in Great Britain in 1992 by
Simon & Schuster Education
Campus 400, Maylands Avenue
Hemel Hempstead, Herts HP2 7EZ

Printed in Great Britain by
BPCC Hazell Books
Paulton and Aylesbury

A catalogue record of this book is available from
the British Library

ISBN 0 7501 0151 2

Series editor: John Day
Editor: Jane Glendening

How many times have you heard people claim that they 'haven't got any energy' or claim to be eating some food in order 'to give me energy', or say that they are switching off the light 'to save energy'? The word <u>energy</u> is used frequently in everyday life, yet its scientific meaning is essentially abstract and quantitative.

Energy is often described as something that makes things happen; but this is a view that looks on energy just as a causal agent which is used up. The realisation that when energy is transformed from one form to another, the total energy of the system remains constant requires a much higher level of understanding.

The concept of energy is a difficult one for young children. It will only develop and deepen through many experiences. A true grasp of the concept will only come when children are well into their secondary school programme of work, yet the gathering of experiences to help develop this should come early in a child's life. Such experiences are the subject of this book.

As in other books in this series children are introduced to the processes of:

- exploring their environment in order to gather experiences at first hand
- manipulating objects and materials
- observing things around them
- questioning and arguing about things
- testing things out and performing simple problem solving activities
- looking for patterns and relationships.

The early pages describe different forms of energy, ways of generating power, and how to measure force and energy. Sometimes they contain activities, but, by and large, they are intended as information pages. The rest of the book primarily concentrates on providing experiences which help develop understanding of light, heat, sound, electricity and magnetism, giving additional information as necessary.

National Curriculum

The book gives comprehensive coverage at Key Stages 1 and 2 of the energy components of:
    NAT3 Materials and their properties
    NAT4 Physical processes
in the new revised Science Curriculum. [These topics were formerly covered in AT11 (Electricity and magnetism), AT13(Energy), AT14 (Sound and music) and AT15 (Using light and electromagnetic radiation) in the original Science Curriculum.] Pursuance of these activities will engage children in the scientific processes set out in NAT1 (Scientific investigation).

Like the other 'Early Start' books, this one provides a concise and comprehensive resource for the National Curriculum. It covers a difficult area of that curriculum, yet, as always, I hope you will find the activities fit naturally into everyday school work, that they are cross-curricular, appeal to children and give real help. Enjoy them!

Roy Richards

Safety in schools

All the activities in this book are safe provided they are properly organised and supervised in accordance with the recommendations of the DES, the Health and Safety Executive, the Association for Science Education, and local authority regulations. Any teachers who are uncertain about safety in scientific and technical work should consult their LEA advisers. They should also read 'Be safe: some aspects of safety in science and technology in primary schools', published by the Association for Science Education.

Always pack away potentially dangerous apparatus and chemicals immediately the activity is over.

Red triangles

Some activities in this book do require extra care and attention. They are marked with a <u>red triangle</u>. Under no circumstances should children be allowed to pursue them unsupervised, particularly during breaks.

Energy is a fundamental concept in physics. It is of enormous importance, and yet it is very difficult to define. Clark Maxwell called it 'the go of things'. Having energy means being able to do something or to bring about some kind of change.

These introductory pages look at different forms of energy and at some activities that will help to give children an insight into each form. They will help to make it clearer what energy is all about.

Potential energy (gravitational stored energy)

An object has more gravitational potential energy the higher up it is.

A toy car placed at A has more potential energy than an identical one at B. When it is released, car A will run further away from the ramp than car B.

'An Early Start to Technology' (pages 34-35) suggests some activities that can be carried out with toy cars and lorries using ramps. It also discusses the variables that are involved.

Here are two things to make that use potential energy.

Moving vehicle

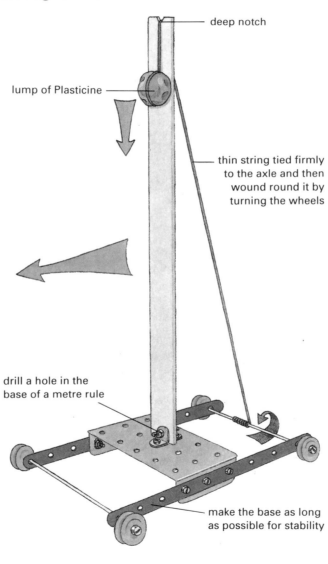

deep notch

lump of Plasticine

thin string tied firmly to the axle and then wound round it by turning the wheels

drill a hole in the base of a metre rule

make the base as long as possible for stability

The falling mass drives the trolley along by causing the back axle to turn.

Carousel

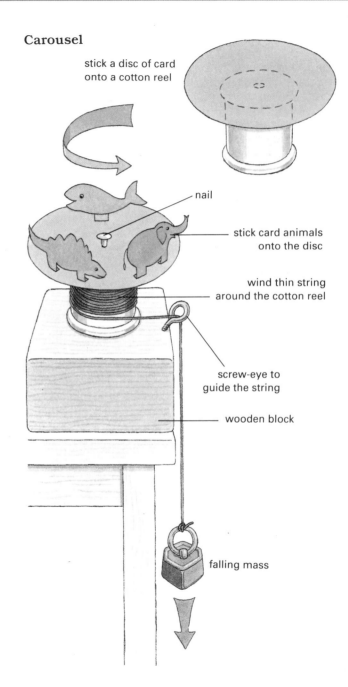

stick a disc of card onto a cotton reel

nail

stick card animals onto the disc

wind thin string around the cotton reel

screw-eye to guide the string

wooden block

falling mass

The falling mass makes the carousel spin.

Kinetic energy

Kinetic energy is the energy an object has when it is moving. The faster an object is moving, the more kinetic energy it has.

The greater the mass of a moving object, the more kinetic energy it has. The kinds of experiments with toy cars and lorries and other moving things in 'An Early Start to Technology' (pages 34–35) will help to give children an understanding of kinetic energy. In practical activities it is important to remember that it is often difficult to separate kinetic energy from potential energy.

Dropping tins

Drop identical empty tin cans from different heights. Listen to the sounds they make on landing. Try a variety of heights, try to memorise the sounds.

Now try a guessing game. Let blindfolded children try to guess the height from which a can is dropped by listening to the sound it makes on landing.

Name	Height can dropped from		
	high	medium	low
James	✓	✗	✓
Cathy	✓	✓	✓

'An Early Start to Technology' (page 78) has more activities on dropping balls.

Stopping a toy lorry

Tie a bag of sand to the end of a toy lorry so that the string attaching the bag to the lorry hangs slack.

Give the lorry a push so that it starts to move freely along.

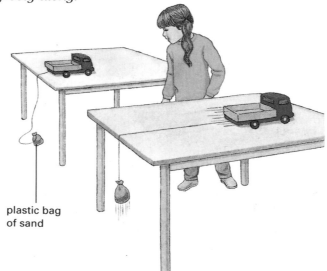

plastic bag of sand

The lorry will be brought to a stop once the string tightens and lifts the load off the ground. The lorry has energy because it is moving. This is kinetic energy and here it has been made to do a job of work, that is, lifting the bag of sand.

What kind of energy ?

What kind of energy does a child sitting at the top of the slide have?

What kind of energy does an arrow flying through the air have?

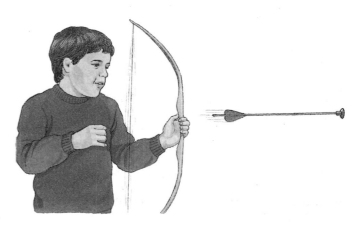

Elastic potential energy is stored in stretched or squashed objects.

The following moving objects are all dependent on elastic potential energy to make them go. Full instructions for making them and details of experiments to carry out with them are given in 'An Early Start to Technology' (pages 33, 36-39, 46, 53).

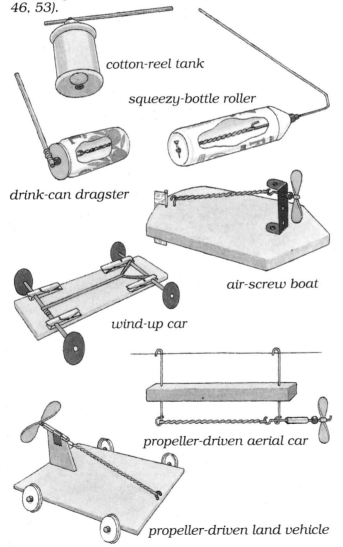

cotton-reel tank

squeezy-bottle roller

drink-can dragster

air-screw boat

wind-up car

propeller-driven aerial car

propeller-driven land vehicle

Stretching a steel spring

Buy a fine steel spring from a scientific supplier. Hang it from a support.

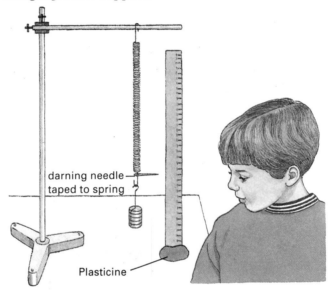

darning needle
taped to spring

Plasticine

Hang masses on the end. It is easier to work directly in newtons (see page 12). Record the change in length of the spring. Plot a graph of extension (in centimetres) against force (in newtons).

extension (centimetres)

force (newtons)

When you remove all the masses, the needle will go back to its original position, showing that the spring is elastic.

Stretching elastic bands

See 'An Early Start to Technology' (page 78) for activities on stretching elastic bands.

How much energy in a tennis ball?

Wet a tennis ball in coloured water.

powder col

Measure the splat it makes when dropped from different heights onto sugar paper.

Height	Size of splat
2.0 m	
1.5 m	

Chemical energy is stored in materials, foods, fuels and batteries. It is released when a chemical reaction takes place.

Food

Foods are used for body building and for providing energy. Ultimately they are burnt up in the tissues to release energy. (This is a chemical reaction.)

See 'An Early Start to Ourselves and Evolution' (pages 12-13) for details and for activities to carry out on food.

Four-stroke petrol engine

The chemical energy locked in petrol is used to drive the piston. Petrol is turned into vapour, mixed with air and ignited by a spark that touches it.

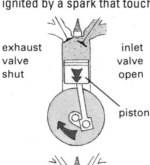

exhaust valve shut   inlet valve open   piston

1 Induction stroke: The piston moves down. This sucks in a mixture of air and petrol vapour.

exhaust valve shut   inlet valve shut

2 Compression stroke: The piston moves up. This compresses the petrol/air mixture.

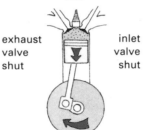

spark plug

exhaust valve shut   inlet valve shut

3 Power stroke: A spark from the spark plug ignites the petrol vapour (a chemical reaction). The force from the explosion pushes the piston down.

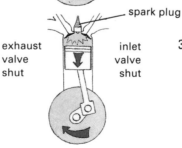

exhaust valve open   inlet valve shut

4 Exhaust stroke: The piston moves up. This clears out the cylinder. The fumes pass through to the exhaust pipe.

Dry-cell battery

A dry-cell battery is a source of chemical energy.

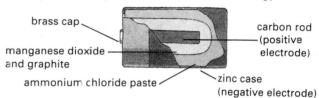

brass cap

manganese dioxide and graphite

ammonium chloride paste

carbon rod (positive electrode)

zinc case (negative electrode)

There is a chemical reaction between the zinc (the case of the cell) and the ammonium chloride paste. (This only happens when the cell is being used.) Electrons flow from the case to the carbon rod. Manganese dioxide around the carbon rod prevents the build up of hydrogen atoms around the rod (see page 71).

Lead-acid accumulator

A dry-cell battery eventually loses its chemical energy – we say it is 'used up' or 'flat'. Its life is finished. Car batteries, on the other hand, can be recharged many times.

The plates (electrodes) are made of lead grids with a paste of spongy lead (negative) and lead oxide (positive) pressed into them. They are surrounded by dilute sulphuric acid. Electrons flow from one to the other.

As the reaction proceeds, the acid is used up to form lead sulphate on the electrodes. This weakens the acid. When the circuit is reversed in the battery, the surfaces of the electrodes change back to lead and lead dioxide and at the same time the acid regains its strength. This recharges the battery.

Light energy

Light energy is given off as rays when an object glows. For example, light energy is given off from the sun. This energy is part of the electromagnetic spectrum (see pages 56–57).

There are many examples of light energy.

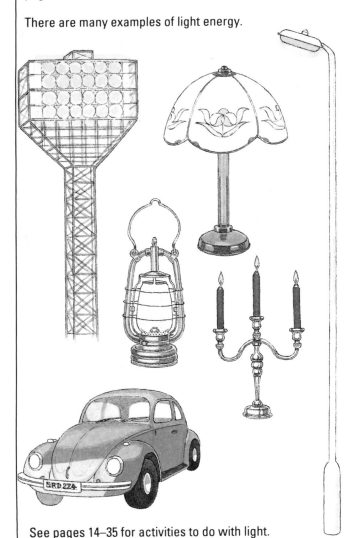

See pages 14–35 for activities to do with light.

A geranium growing on a window sill is dependent on the sun for the energy for its growth.

The geranium's leaves are large, flat and green. This provides a large surface area for the uptake of carbon dioxide from the air. The absorbed carbon dioxide then combines with water to form sugars.

This reaction is called photosynthesis. The energy for it is provided by sunlight. The chlorophyll or green colouring in leaves helps to speed up this reaction. (It is called a catalyst .) The same process can be fuelled by artificial lighting.

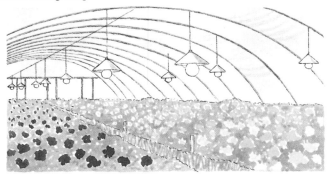

The 'storage' of energy, as sugars, is fundamental to plant growth and ultimately to the growth of the animals that feed on plants, as well as to the animals that prey, in turn, on these animals.

See page 48 of 'An Early Start to Ourselves and Evolution' for activities to do with photosynthesis.

Heat energy

Heat energy is given off when the molecules in a substance vibrate.

You cannot see the molecules vibrating at the end of a red hot poker, but they are, and the manifestation of their movement is the red glow. If you hold a poker in a fire, the heat spreads higher and higher up the poker. This is an example of conduction of heat.

<u>Convection</u> currents are set up in a room by, for example, a convector heater. The warm air from the convector heater rises to replace the colder air above. This colder air settles in turn to be heated and then rise.

warm air

cool air

<u>Radiated</u> heat travels directly through the air. It hits and warms objects in its path.

See pages 36–43 for further explanation and activities on heat energy.

Sound energy

Sound is the energy transferred from a vibrating source by waves of vibrating air.

If you set a tuning fork vibrating, waves of vibrations are set up. They move backwards and forwards to produce alternate sections of compressed and expanded air.

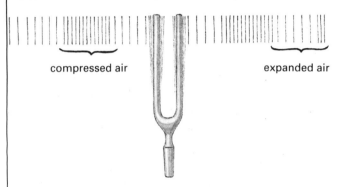

compressed air   expanded air

An aircraft moving through air pushes waves of air ahead of it. These are called compression waves. As these approach the speed of sound, they become sound waves and an explosive sound is heard. The aircraft is said to be passing through the sound barrier. The energy of the bang is clearly discernible.

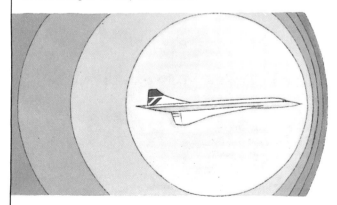

See pages 44–55 for further explanation and activities on sound.

Electrical energy

This is the energy due to the movement of electric charge. For example, the energy of electricity flowing through a lamp is converted to heat and light energy.

There are innumerable examples of the uses of electrical energy.

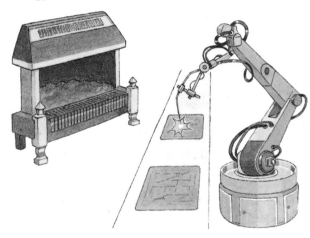

See pages 58–85 for further explanation and activities on electricity.

Nuclear energy

This is the energy stored in the nucleus of an atom. If a nucleus is split or two nuclei are joined together energy is released.

nuclear explosion

The following are all examples of ways in which energy can be captured and converted into another form.

Water power

A water wheel makes use of the kinetic energy of moving water.

In an overshot water wheel the water falls on to the wheel from above.

In an undershot water wheel the water flows beneath.

For many centuries, water wheels were one of the main ways of providing the energy; for example, to grind corn to make flour.

'An Early Start to Technology' (page 59) shows how to make a model water wheel.

Waves also have considerable energy. Children are familiar with surfers using the power of waves to carry themselves along.

Tidal energy

The energy of the waves as they bob up and down can be used to drive electrical generators.

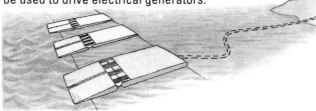

Alternatively, the sea surging into a bay or estuary with the tide can be locked in by a suitable barrier. At an appropriate time, the trapped sea water can be let out and the energy used to drive turbines to generate electricity.

The estuary of the river La Rance in France has a famous tidal barrier.

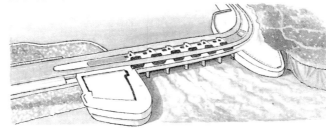

The same principle is used in a dam. The generating station is at its base to make use of the energy from falling water.

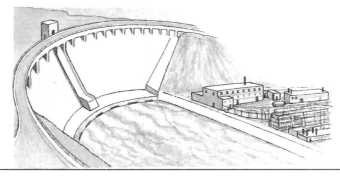

Wind power

Harnessing the kinetic energy of the wind is an old method of power generation now much advocated by those concerned with reducing pollution in the environment. 'An Early Start to Technology' (page 58) has sections on 'Wind power' and 'Using the wind' which describe how to make windmills.

Nowadays the wind energy is usually converted to electrical energy by generators driven by rotors on tall masts.

Geothermal energy

Geothermal energy is the heat energy inside the Earth. Molten rock beneath the Earth's crust is kept hot by the radioactive decay of elements in the Earth's core.

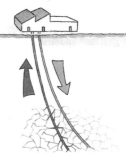

There is a gradation in heat below the Earth's surface. For example, the temperature at the bottom of a 2000 metre oil-well can be 60°C higher than that at the surface.

Water trickles down through porous rock. It is heated up and turned to steam. Geothermal wells tap this steam, which can be used to drive turbines or directly for heating.

Fossil energy

Coal, gas and oil are all fossil fuels.

Many millions of years ago, plants captured the sun's energy during photosynthesis and grew to form the forests covering the Earth's surface. In time, much of this timber and other plant life was compressed to form coal.

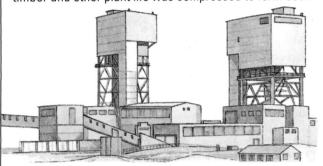

This coal is now dug up to fuel power stations, or it is burnt directly in homes and industry to provide heat.

The remains of tiny plants and animals deposited on the ocean bed millions of years ago built up in layers to eventually form oil and gas. These are extracted by drilling.

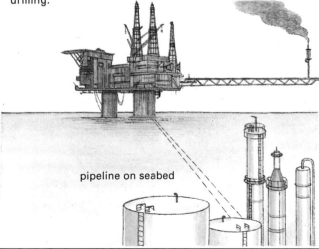

pipeline on seabed

Once refined, oil products in the form of petroleum, diesel fuel, kerosene or liquid petroleum gas are used to provide energy.

They are popular because they are easily transportable, give a lot of energy for their volume, and burn smoothly. However, like coal, they pollute the atmosphere by giving off carbon dioxide and sulphur dioxide among other things.

Nuclear power

Nuclear power stations use uranium fuel rods. These are lowered into the reactor where the uranium nuclei are split up, releasing large amounts of energy, in a process called fission.

A nuclear power station is very complex and therefore expensive to build. Although it does not produce gases to pollute the atmosphere, it does produce radioactive waste products which need very careful treatment and disposal.

The energy released by a nuclear power station is used to generate steam, which in turn generates electricity. Energy is released gradually in a nuclear reactor. In a nuclear bomb it is released all at once.

Solar power

Energy from the Sun can be used directly to heat water.

Some houses have solar panels on their roofs. Each panel has tubes running through it carrying water. The water is heated up by the Sun. It may not become very hot, but subsidiary heat sources can be used to boost it to the temperature needed.

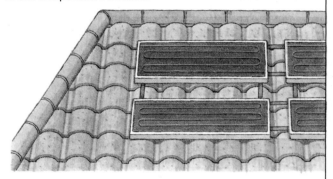

On a much bigger scale, large solar reflectors are used to focus the Sun's rays on a small area. The very high temperatures produced are even sufficient to work a furnace.

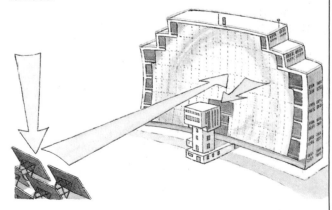

'An Early Start to Technology' (page 73) shows how to make a solar cooker.

Children are aware of the phenomenon of weightlessness through hearing about astronauts and space travel. It is therefore necessary to distinguish between the concepts of mass and weight at an early age.

<u>The mass of an object is the amount of stuff in it. Mass is measured in grams (g) and kilograms (kg).</u>

If you were placed in an equal pan balance on the Earth, and then on the Moon, the balance would be the same in each case.

In this instance, masses are being compared. Your mass on the moon is the same as your mass on the earth.

mass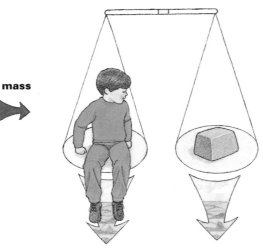

under the force of the Earth's gravity

under the force of the Moon's gravity

<u>The weight of an object is the force exerted on it by a gravitational field. Weight is measured in newtons (N).</u>

weight

If you were to stand on bathroom scales on the Earth, and then on the Moon, the readings would be different.

This is because the moon's gravitational pull is about one-sixth that of the earth. So on the Moon you would weigh about one-sixth of what you weigh on the Earth.

Here weights, not masses, are being compared.

under the force of the Earth's gravity

under the force of the Moon's gravity

Since weight is a force, we would expect it to be measured in units of force. The metric unit of force is the <u>newton</u> (N).

One newton is the force which produces a change in velocity (or an acceleration) of 1 metre per second in each second when applied to a mass of 1 kilogram.

Gravity produces an acceleration of about 9.8 metres per second in each second at the Earth's surface. It takes a force of 9.8 newtons to produce an acceleration of 9.8 metres per second in each second, in a mass of 1 kilogram.

Roughly speaking, a mass of 1 kilogram has a weight (force) of about 10 newtons on the Earth. Gravity on the Moon is about one-sixth as strong as on Earth, so the kilogram mass would only weigh 10/6 newtons there. However its mass would still be 1 kilogram.

Energy is measured in joules (J). The joule is defined in terms of the newton.

One joule is the amount of work done when a force of 1 newton moves an object a distance of 1 metre in the direction of the force.

What is work?

If a force pushes on an object but does not move it, there is no energy change. That is, no work has been done.

car (brake on)

If a force pushes on an object and moves it, there is an energy change. That is, work has been done.

car (brake off)

'Work' is the term used for the amount of the change.

Example

$$\text{work done} = \text{force} \times \begin{array}{l}\text{distance moved}\\\text{in the direction of the force}\end{array}$$

If a force of 50 newtons is needed to move a truck 5 metres along the floor then:

work done = 50 newtons x 5 metres
= 250 joules

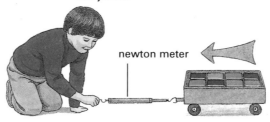

newton meter

See 'An Early Start to the Environment' (pages 14-15) for methods of making force meters. See 'An Early Start to Ourselves and Evolution' (page 16) for activities on measuring the amount of work done.

Dropping objects

Some things have energy by virtue of their position. They have gravitational potential energy.

How much energy do they have?

The weight of an apple is roughly 1 newton. The potential energy gain of an apple falling through one metre is:

1m

potential energy = 1 newton x 1 metre
= 1 joule

Power

Power is the amount of work done in a certain time.

$$\text{power} = \frac{\text{work done}}{\text{time taken}}$$

Power is measured in watts (W). One watt of power is produced when one joule of work is done in one second.

A 100 watt light bulb converts 100 joules of electrical energy into light and heat every second.

Power ratings of some common objects:

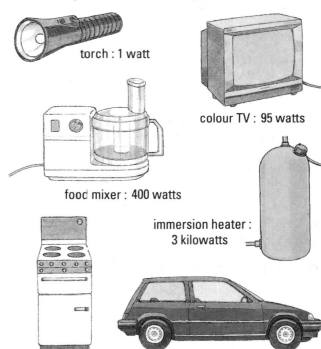

torch : 1 watt

colour TV : 95 watts

food mixer : 400 watts

immersion heater : 3 kilowatts

cooker : 6 kilowatts

car : 60 kilowatts

See 'An Early Start to Ourselves and Evolution' (page 16) for activities related to power.

How many sources of light can the children find?

Make drawings and paintings of each. Arrange them as a display. Talk about the different sources. Some get hot; others, such as fluorescent tubes, only get warm; and the glowing digital display on the clock radio is cold.

Sources of light

sun

fluorescent tube

light bulb

candle

gas lighter

match

stars

oil lamp

torch

motorbike headlights

bedside clock radio

We are concerned in this section with sources that make their own light, that is <u>self-luminous</u> sources. The light they emit travels into our eyes.

Most objects are seen by reflected light which has fallen on them from a self-luminous source. Such objects are <u>non-luminous</u>.

Children often think that light travels from their eye to an object in order for them to see the object. The reality of seeing things by reflected light only comes from a lot of experience and good teaching.

The car is seen because it reflects light into the eye.

If light from a source cannot pass through an object there is a dark area on the other side of that object. This is its shadow.

Shadow play

Play with light from the sun to make shadows.

Make funny-shaped shadows. Whose is funniest?
Who can make the longest shadow?
Who can make the shortest shadow?
Can you hide your shadow?
Can you jump on your shadow?
Stand upside down and make a shadow.
Can you make a shadow with four arms and four legs?
Can you move without your shadow moving?
Can you stand with your shadow in front of you?
Can you stand with your shadow behind you?

Use objects to make shadows

Try to make the largest and the smallest possible shadows using a variety of objects.

Play with light from artificial fixed sources to make shadows.

Make profile silhouettes

Pin a large sheet of white paper to the wall. Darken the room. Seat a child in front of a desk lamp. Adjust his or her position so that the best possible shadow of their profile is cast on to the paper. Draw round this shadow. Later it can be coloured in.

Do this for each member of the class. Can the children recognise each other from their silhouettes?

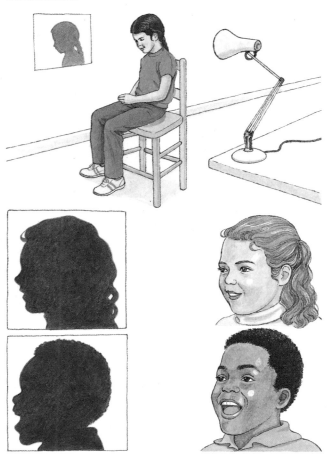

Play with shadows on the wall

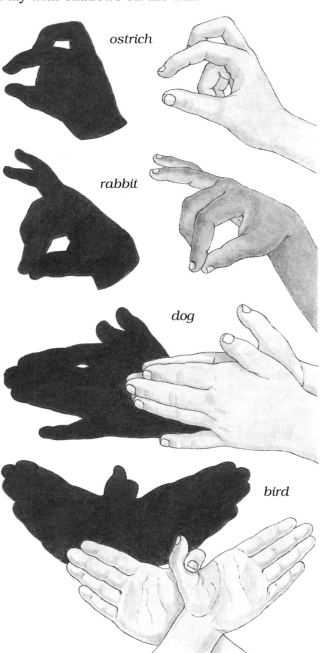

ostrich

rabbit

dog

bird

Shadow puppets

Make some shadow puppets from card. Attach them to rods.

Perform well-known children's stories such as 'The Tale of Peter Rabbit'.

typical Javanese shadow-puppet

Shadow box

Make a box to investigate shadows.

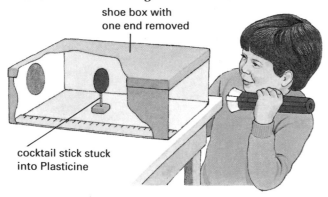

shoe box with one end removed

cocktail stick stuck into Plasticine

Use various card shapes stuck to cocktail sticks.

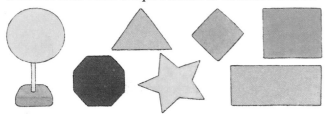

Try making a shadow the same size as the shape.
Try making a shadow twice as big as the shape.
Try making a shadow smaller than the shape.
Try rotating each shape. What happens?

Mould some 3D shapes from Plasticine.

Try them out in your shadow box.

Light travels in straight lines

The traditional way to demonstrate that light travels in straight lines is to line up three identical cards, each of which has a tiny hole in its centre. A long piece of cotton is threaded through the holes.

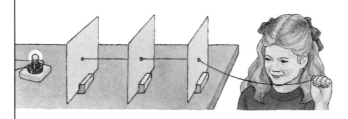

The cards are positioned so that a lighted bulb can be seen through <u>all three holes</u>.

Drawing the cotton thread tight does not disturb the cards. This shows that as the thread is straight, the light rays must be straight too.

Although this experiment is clear to adults and to some juniors, it is too sophisticated for many young children and just puzzles them.

Light from a small source

If a light source is small, like a bulb filament, then the shadow cast is sharp. This is because all the light rays going past the object casting the shadow are effectively coming from the same place – a point source.

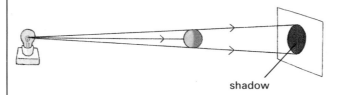

shadow

The dark area is called the umbra (Latin for dark).

The size of the shadow depends on the size of the object and the distance of the object and the screen from the light source:

$$\frac{\text{shadow size}}{\text{object size}} = \frac{\text{shadow distance from source}}{\text{object distance from source}}$$

Light from a big source (i.e. not a point source)

If the light does not come from a point source, then the shadow is not so sharp. Some of the light can get round the object creating what is called the penumbra.

Children will have discovered this from some of the experiments on page 16.

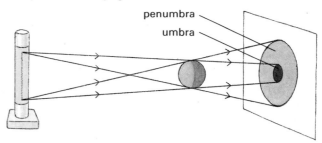

penumbra
umbra

Eclipses of the Sun

When the moon comes between the Earth and the Sun you get an eclipse.

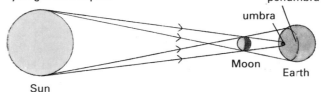

penumbra
umbra
Moon
Earth
Sun

Seen from the umbra the eclipse is total. That is, the sun is completely obscured, and everything goes dark.

Seen from the penumbra the eclipse is partial. That is, the sun is partially obscured, and everything goes darker.

Look for reflections

Make drawings and paintings of reflections you find.

Look in the kitchen.

Look in the bathroom.

Look elsewhere.

What happens when light hits an object?

Light rays travel in straight lines. When they hit a material there are three things that can happen, depending on the type of material.

1 The light is <u>absorbed</u>. Some heat energy passes into the material and it becomes slightly warm.

2 The light travels <u>through</u> the material, in some cases changing direction. When this happens, it is called <u>refraction</u>.

3 The light bounces off the material. This is <u>reflection</u>.

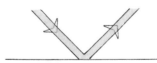

Often a combination of these things happens. For example, when you look at a window, you see through it <u>and</u> may see your reflection at the same time.

More about reflection

Light is reflected from mirrors, pools of water, shop windows, car windscreens, polished metal and other objects.

When a light ray strikes a mirror it is reflected outwards at an angle. A line drawn perpendicular to the surface of the mirror at the point where the light strikes the mirror is called the 'normal'.

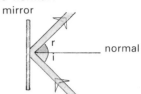

The angle of incidence (i) equals the angle of reflection (r).

Light rays falling on a smooth surface are reflected parallel to one another.

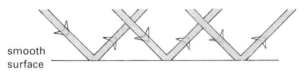

Light falling on a rough surface is reflected in lots of different directions.

This irregular reflection is more soothing to the eye than regular reflection. Think of the difference between brushed and polished stainless steel.

A new plastic food box is relatively transparent. As it becomes worn and scratched, it reflects light irregularly and becomes more opaque.

Playing with mirrors

Where do you have to position a mirror to see the ceiling light?

Where do you have to position a mirror to see the person behind you?

Where do you have to position a mirror to be able to see down the corridor?

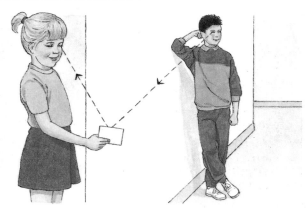

Where do you have to position a mirror to see over things?

Fix a large mirror at the front of the classroom, at the same height as the children's heads. Ask each child in turn to say who he or she can see.

By this means, the equality of angles of incidence and reflection will be evident.

Look in a mirror. Touch your nose. Touch an eye. Touch an ear. Touch an eyelid. Comb your hair. Wink at yourself.

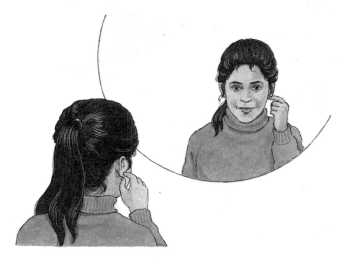

In each case the right and left sides are swopped. If you touch your right ear, it looks as though you are touching your left ear. This is called 'lateral inversion'.

This is an example of a word which is often seen laterally inverted.

Reflections using one mirror

Make some patterns to complete with a mirror.

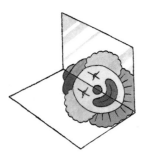

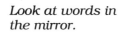

Look at words in the mirror.

Try the mirror on these two names. What happens?

Alphabet reflections

Some letters have vertical symmetry. One half mirrors the other half across a vertical axis.

mirror here

Some letters have horizontal symmetry. One half mirrors the other half across an horizontal axis.

 mirror here

Examine the letters of the alphabet for vertical and horizontal symmetry.

ABCDEFGHIJKL
MNOPQRSTUV
WXYZ

Make some symmetrical words.

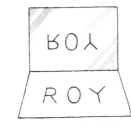

CHOICE

MUM

Reflections using two mirrors

Join two mirrors together using masking tape stuck along their backs.

Make some patterns to put between the mirror fronts.

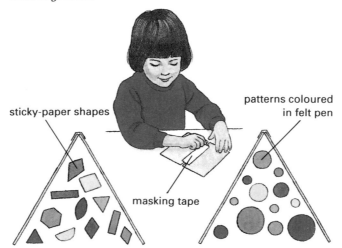

sticky-paper shapes

patterns coloured in felt pen

masking tape

Place an object between the two mirrors and vary the angle between the mirrors.

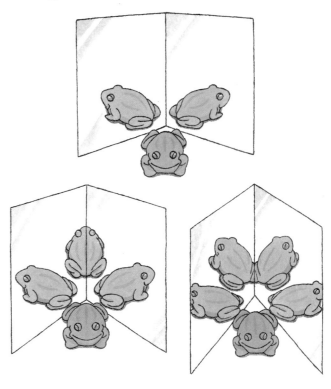

As the angle decreases and the mirrors get nearer to each other, the number of images increases, producing a kaleidoscopic effect.

You can show the mirrors in a kaleidoscope to the children by breathing into the peephole at the end as this will cause the mirrors inside to cloud over.

Make a kaleidoscope

1 *Join three mirrors with two pieces of masking tape, so that the reflective surfaces all face down.*

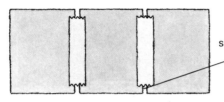

leave just enough space for the mirrors to meet when you bend them

2 *Turn the two outside mirrors up to form a triangular prism. Tape the top edges together.*

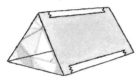

This is your kaleidoscope.

3 *Cover one end of the kaleidoscope with a piece of clear polythene cut from a freezer bag. Hold it in place with an elastic band.*

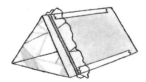

4 *Drop small pieces of coloured card into the kaleidoscope. Cover the open end with a piece of greaseproof paper. Stick the edges down with masking tape.*

5 *Hold the kaleidoscope to the light. Rotate it to see the pattern.*

Make a periscope

You can make a simple periscope which will allow you to peep over walls by attaching a mirror to the end of a metre rule with bulldog clips.

You can make a more effective periscope using two mirrors.

1 *Cut a piece of card three times as long as one mirror but the same width. Tape the mirror to one end.*

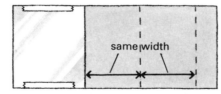

same width

2 *Fold the card into a triangular prism with the mirror facing outwards. Make sure you have a 90° angle at the corner opposite the mirror so that the two sides without a mirror are the same length. Tape this corner.*

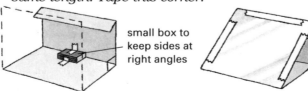

small box to keep sides at right angles

3 *Repeat the procedure to make another triangular prism.*

4 *Cut a piece of card as shown below, and fold it to make a tube.*

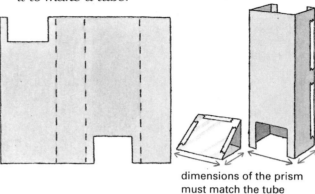

dimensions of the prism must match the tube

5 *Insert a triangular prism at each end of the card tube so that the mirrors face the windows. Tape the prisms in position.*

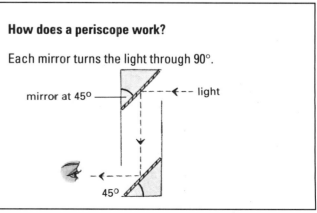

How does a periscope work?

Each mirror turns the light through 90°.

mirror at 45° — light

45°

Where is the image in a mirror?

Arrange a mirror so that the children can walk toward and away from it.

Can they find a relationship between their distance from the mirror and the distance their image appears behind the mirror?

Does their image get smaller or larger as they get further away from it?

Is the image in the glass?

Wedge a sheet of well polished glass into Plasticine to hold it vertically on a sheet of paper.

Mark a cross with a pencil in front of the glass. Look its reflection. This is the image.

Draw a cross behind the glass over the image. Measure the distance of both crosses from the glass.

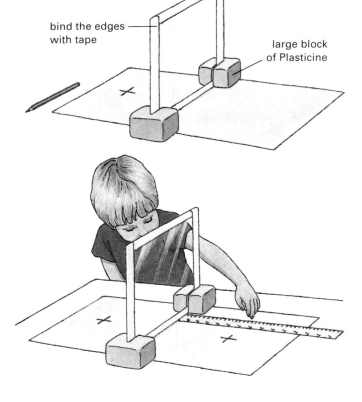

bind the edges with tape

large block of Plasticine

Try again with crosses in different positions. Try varying the distance from the glass.

The children will discover that the distance the image appears behind the glass is the same as the distance of the cross in front of the glass.

Ghostly candle

Remove a picture from its frame to leave just the glass and frame. Hold the frame upright with a clamp or wedge it between two piles of books.

view from this side of the glass

Place an unlit candle on one side and a jam jar of water the other. Look through the frame from the candle side. Ask someone to move the jar until the candle's image appears in it.

Light the candle. It will appear to be burning in the water!

Just a spoon

You need a new shiny spoon for this. A large tablespoon is good, but a large <u>round</u> serving spoon is even better.

Make a drawing of what you look like in each surface.

Hold the spoon some distance from you, say 30 cm. Look into the bowl of the spoon – the concave surface.

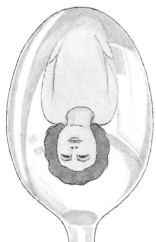

The image is upside down and small.

Still looking into the bowl of the spoon, bring the spoon slowly towards you until it is very close to your eye.

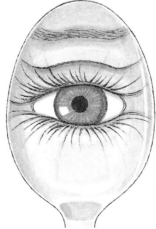

The image gradually becomes blurred and then suddenly turns the right way up to give a picture of your eye which is greatly enlarged.

Hold the spoon some distance from you. Look into its back – the convex surface.

The image is small and upright and there is a wide field of view. You can probably see much of the room behind you.

A swimming pool is deeper than it looks. A spoon at the bottom of the washing-up bowl looks nearer than it is, and you get your sleeve wet!

Put a ruler in a tank of water.

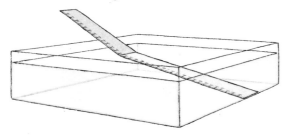

Put a pencil in a jam-jar of water.

The apparent bending, or refraction, of the ruler and the pencil will be clear.

Make a coin reappear

1 *Put a coin in the bottom of a cup and move back until it just disappears from sight.*

2 *Ask a friend to slowly pour water in the cup. Keep your eye on the cup.*

The coin reappears.

These sectional diagrams explain what happens.

With no water in the cup, no light from the coin can reach your eye.

The light is refracted by the water, and so the light reaches the eye. The coin and the bottom of the cup are seen nearer to the top of the cup than they actually are.

What is refraction?

Light travels fastest through a vacuum – at 300 million metres per second (3×10^8 metres per second). It travels almost as fast through air. Water, glass and perspex slow it down much more.

When light crosses from one material to another, it may change direction. This bending of light rays is called refraction.

You can trace the path of a ray of light as it enters and leaves a glass block. It is then easy to trace the ray through the block by joining your two original lines.

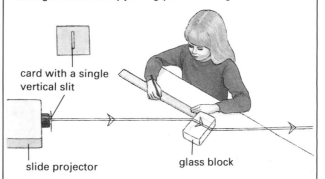

card with a single vertical slit

slide projector

glass block

The bending or refraction of the ray as it crosses from the air into the glass can be explained by a change in speed.

An analogy is a car driving into mud. If the car hits the mud head on it slows the car down. If the car hits the mud at an angle, the wheels on one side of the car hit the mud first, these slow down before the wheels on the other side of the car thus causing the car to turn slightly. A similar effect occurs when the car leaves the mud.

> Transparent: things which can be seen through clearly.
>
> Translucent: things which let light through, but we only see through them in a blurred way.
>
> Opaque: things which let no light through.

Examination of these phenomena is fun if tackled as a large-scale sorting and separating exercise. Group materials into those which can be seen through, those which cannot and those which are translucent.

Investigate different types of fabric

chiffon

cotton

hessian

towelling

wool

silk

gaberdine

Look at a collection of glass

Sort a collection of papers

toffee paper

writing paper

sugar paper

tissue paper

card

greaseproof paper

newspaper

corrugated card

toilet paper

Investigate various liquids

tap water

soapy water

water shaken with soil

tea

powder paint

orange squash

olive oil

coffee

tomato sauce

milk

cola

flour + water glue

Sort out different plastics

These activities will lead to lots of discussion. Factors such as how thick things are, how bright the light is, whether there are air spaces in the material (such as in a woollen garment) and so on may arise.

Investigate how curved surfaces magnify things

Try drops of water on a glossy magazine page.

fish and dead seabirds are — droplet of water
wall in the North Sea. N**O**ne
ct sources of the problems are,
l pollut**nt** can't be doing any
orts on the obvious first step.

If you draw a circle with wax crayon on a glass slide, it will hold a water drop.

oned fish and dead seabirds are
is not well in the North Sea. No one
e exact source **O**f the problems are, — wax-crayon circle
lux of pollutants can't be doing any — drop of water
n reports on the obvious first step.

Move the slide up and down above some print until the letters appear clearly in the water drop.

Why does your finger look bigger if you stick it into a jam-jar of water?

What causes this? Is it the water, the glass, or the shape?

Look at some convex lenses

Remember, convex lenses are fatter in the middle than at the outside edge.

Observe how a convex lens magnifies things.

Devise a test to compare their magnifying power.

You could draw some parallel lines on paper to help you with your comparison.

This lens is magnifying by two times.

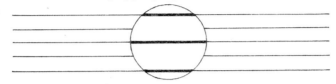

Make some magnifiers

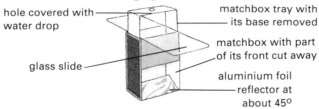

bent wire — water drop

Try glycerine and olive oil as lenses.

Make a matchbox magnifier.

hole covered with — matchbox tray with
water drop — its base removed

— matchbox with part
of its front cut away

glass slide —

aluminium foil
— reflector at
about 45°

Make a foil magnifier by folding a strip of kitchen foil in half four times to give a fairly rigid metal strip. Make a hole at one end with a knitting needle. Then secure the strip in position as shown.

Place a drop of water over the hole.

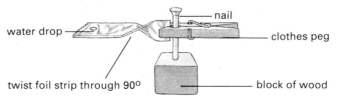

— nail
water drop —
— clothes peg

twist foil strip through 90° — block of wood

Lenses

Lenses bend (refract) light. Convex lenses are fatter in the middle than at the edge. They cause light rays to converge on a common point: they are focused.

Where the rays meet is called the principal focus.

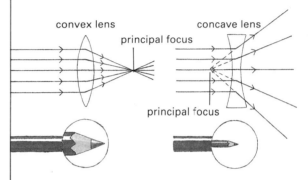

convex lens — concave lens
principal focus

principal focus

Concave lenses cause light rays to spread out or diverge.

Things seen through a concave lens appear smaller.

Focal length of a convex lens

The distance from the principal focus to the centre of the lens is called the focal length.

A rough and ready way of finding the focal point of a convex lens is to hold it facing a window and move a plain sheet of white card behind it. Once you have a fairly clear picture on the card then the distance from the lens to the card is the focal length of the lens.

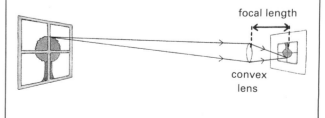

focal length

convex lens

Set up a display of objects containing lenses.

Make a telescope

You will need three lenses:

convex lens of short focal length (about 50mm)
convex lens of long focal length (about 300mm)
concave lens of short focal length (about 50mm)

You can buy lenses from a scientific supplier.

Insert the two convex lenses at either end of a long block of Plasticine. They must be vertical with their centres in line. You will need to move the eyepiece back and forth until you can see a good image of a distant object. Put the concave lens immediately in front of the eyepiece. This will give you an upright image.

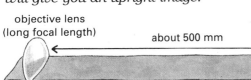

objective lens
(long focal length)

about 500 mm

eye piece
(short focal length)

concave lens

block of Plasticine

Make a pin-hole camera

1 *Remove the end from a shoe-box, including the end bar of the lid. Fix the lid to the base with tape.*

remove the ends from
the box and the lid

2 *Cut a flat piece of balsa-wood to fit very <u>closely</u> inside the end of the box. Remove the central part from the wood.*

balsa wood

3 *Fix this frame to a handle and cover it with a greaseproof paper screen.*

greaseproof-
paper
screen

tiny hole

4 *Make a tiny hole in the centre of the remaining end of the shoe box. Insert the screen at the other end.*

5 *Hold the box facing a lit candle. Move the greaseproof paper screen to and fro until you can see an image of the candle on the screen. You will see the candle flame flickering — upside down.*

insert the
screen

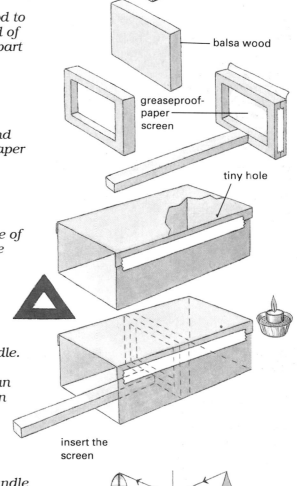

Light rays from the top of the candle hit the bottom of the screen. Light rays from the bottom of the candle hit the top of the screen.

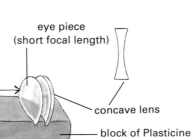

The Victorians were very fond of optical toys. Many of these depended on the ability of the brain to retain images for a short time.

The workings of the eye are described in 'An Early Start to Ourselves and Evolution' (pages 24-25) and the beginning of work on image retention is described there.

Here are some activities that stress the idea of image retention and introduce children to some simple technology.

Make a flick book

Cut about thirty pieces of thin card. Join the card pieces together by punching two holes in each piece. Then tie with thin string and bind with sticky tape. Alternatively you could use a small notebook.

Draw a series of action pictures in sequence. For example, show a bird flying or clock hands turning. Flick the pages of the book rapidly. The eye retains each passing picture for a short period of time, thus creating an illusion of movement.

Make a thaumatrope

A thaumatrope is a spinning piece of card with a picture on each side. Traditionally, you have a bird on one side and a cage on the other. Spinning the card gives the impression that the bird is in the cage. Another favourite is a goldfish appearing in a goldfish bowl.

In this example, you can put the stripes on a tiger. Note that the back picture needs to be drawn upside down.

punched holes

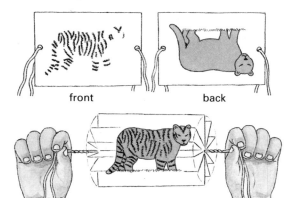

front   back

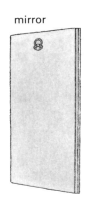

Make a phenakistoscope

This is another toy that depends on the brain retaining the moving images that are presented to it.

1 Draw a large disc with a diameter of 200 mm.

2 Draw an inner circle on the disc of about 160 mm diameter. Draw a series of moving pictures in the outer ring as shown. It is important that they are evenly spaced.

Then cut a series of viewing slits with a craft knife.

3 Push a hatpin or a nail through the centre of the disc and into a cork. Put a bead either side of the card to help it run smoothly.

4 Hold the disc up to a mirror. Make sure there is a good light behind you. Twirl the disc by striking the edge. Look through the slits. Watch the moving pictures in the mirror.

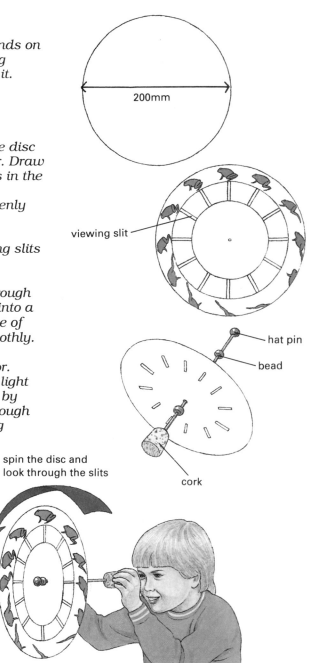

200mm

viewing slit

hat pin
bead

spin the disc and look through the slits

cork

mirror

Make a zoetrope

1 Draw a circle with a diameter of 175 mm on thick card. Cut out this disc.

2 Cut a strip of black card 560 mm long and 160 mm wide. Make slits in this with a craft knife.

Each slit must be 50 mm long, 4 mm wide and 42 mm from its neighbour. The top of each slit should be 25 mm from the top of the card.

3 Stick a length of broad sticky tape all along the lower edge of the strip with half its width projecting over the edge of the black paper. Cut out nicks in the tape all the way round.

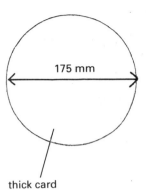

thick card

175 mm

4 Bend the strip of black card around the card disc and join the overlap with another piece of tape. Stick down the sticky-tape tabs.

5 Push a hat pin or nail through the centre of the base and into a cork. Put a bead either side of the card so that it spins smoothly. Put the cork into a bottle weighted with sand.

6 Trace the two strips of figures below onto a piece of paper. Join them up. Place your strip in the zoetrope so that it goes round the inside of the drum just below the slits.

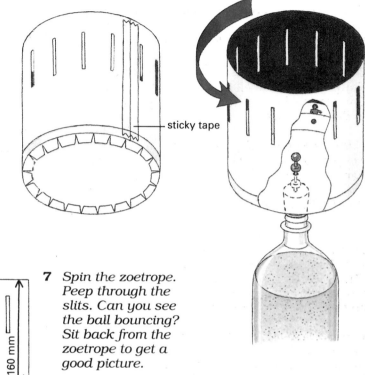

sticky tape

7 Spin the zoetrope. Peep through the slits. Can you see the ball bouncing? Sit back from the zoetrope to get a good picture.

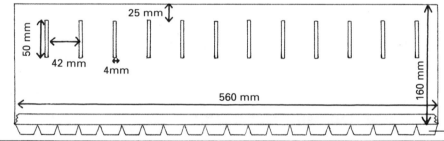

25 mm

50 mm

42 mm

4mm

560 mm

160 mm

sticky-tape tabs

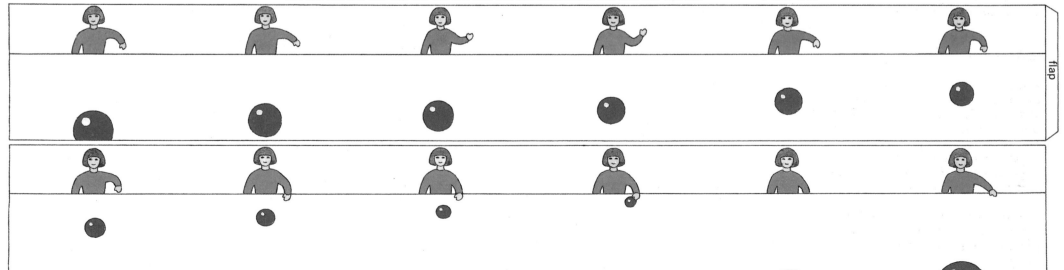

flap

Isaac Newton (1642-1727) wrote 'In the year 1666 (at which time I applied myself to the grinding of optick glasses of figures other than spherical) I procured me a triangular glass prism, to try therewith the celebrated phenomenon of colours.

'And in order thereto, having darkened my chamber and made a very small hole in my window-shuts to let in a convenient quantity of the Sun's light, I placed my prism at its entrance, that it might thereby be refracted to the opposite wall. It was at first a very pleasing divertissement, to view the vivid and intense colours produced thereby.'

Just like Isaac Newton, you can produce a rainbow or spectrum with a glass prism. A slide projector makes a good light source. Insert a card with a narrow slit cut in it into the projector so that you get a thin beam of light.

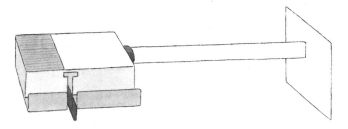

Position the triangular prism on a pile of books so that it is at the same height as the beam of light.

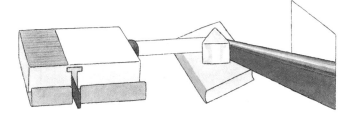

Turn the projector through about 40° to bring the spectrum onto the screen. Then turn the prism slightly to get the best spectrum you can. You should be able to get quite bright colours.

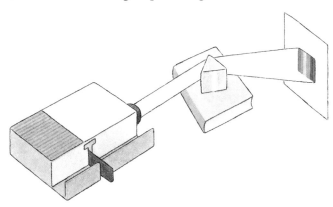

The prism splits white light into its constituent colours.

The mnemonic:

   Richard **O**f **Y**ork **G**ave **B**attle **I**n **V**ain

is useful for remembering the initial letters of colours in their order.

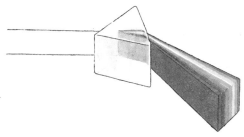

Make a spectrum using a mirror

You can make a large spectrum on the classroom ceiling with a projector and a mirror if you can black out the classroom. This is a bit fiddly to do, but persevere as it is worth the effort (and it's easier the second time around).

Angle the projector to point down at a mirror in a bowl of water. Experiment with the angle of the mirror in the bowl. Once you are satisfied with the spectrum you get on the ceiling, keep the mirror in place with a piece of Plasticine.

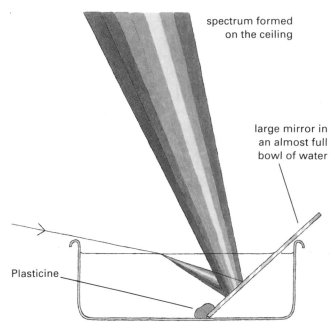

spectrum formed on the ceiling

large mirror in an almost full bowl of water

Plasticine

Disturb the surface of the water. What happens to the spectrum?

Pieces from a glass chandelier held to the light show a spectrum at their edge as does a triangular glass prism.

Primary colours of light

The primary colours of <u>light</u> are red, green and blue.

If two beams of primary colours overlap, you get a secondary colour: yellow, magenta or cyan. Combining all three primary colours makes white light.

Each colour has a complementary colour, the one on the opposite side of white. So magenta is the complementary colour of green.

If you mix two complementary colours together you get white light.

Mixing two beams of light together involves colour <u>addition.</u> Your eyes see the combined effects of the two beams.

Primary colours of paints

The primary colours of <u>paint</u> are magenta, yellow and cyan.

If you mix two primary colours together, you get secondary colours. For paints these are red, green and blue.

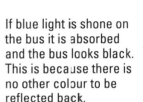

As with light, each colour has a complementary colour. Blue is the complementary colour of yellow.

When you mix two complementary colours you should get grey.

In reality, you often do not get grey because the pigments are not pure.

Mixing cyan and yellow makes green. Cyan reflects green as well as blue light. Yellow reflects red and green light. Mixed together the paints look green only because green is reflected by both. The mixed paints have 'taken away' red and blue to leave green. This is called colour <u>subtraction</u>.

Reflecting colour

A red toy bus looks red because it reflects the red part of white light, and absorbs all the other colours.

If blue light is shone on the bus it is absorbed and the bus looks black. This is because there is no other colour to be reflected back.

If magenta (which is made of red and blue) is shone on the bus the red is reflected and the bus appears red. The blue is absorbed.

Yellow things reflect the red and green parts that make up yellow and absorb the blue parts of white light.

So if you shine cyan (which is made of blue and green) on a yellow banana, it will look green because it absorbs the blue light and reflects the green.

Examining colour

Take a shoe box and cut an oblong-shaped hole in the lid and an inspection hole in the end panel, as shown. Place a large piece of white card diagonally across the box to serve as a viewing platform.

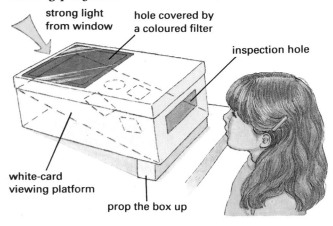

strong light from window

hole covered by a coloured filter

inspection hole

white-card viewing platform

prop the box up

Place differently coloured pieces of paper on the viewing platform. Put a red filter over the top hole. What effect does the red light have on the colours of the pieces of paper when you look at them through the viewing hole? Try other colours of filter and keep a record.

Filter	Effect on coloured pieces of paper					
	red	orange	yellow	green	blue	purple
red						
green						
blue						
blue/green						
magenta						
yellow						

As we showed on the previous page, objects appear coloured because they absorb part of the spectrum and reflect back the rest. A blue piece of paper viewed in the red light will appear black. This is because the red light is absorbed and there is no blue present to be reflected.

Try holding coloured filters up to the light in overlapping pairs.

Red filter lets only red through.
Blue filter lets only blue through.
Green filter lets only green through.
Blue-green filter lets blue and green through.
Magenta filter lets red and blue through.
Yellow lets through red and green.

So with yellow and magenta filters overlapping red will be seen. With yellow and blue-green filters overlapping green will be seen.

Common yellow, the kind reflected by paints or found in spotlights, actually contains red and green. True yellow from the yellow part of the spectrum, or found in sodium street lamps, is not a mixture of red and green.

Grass hit by a spotlight at night absorbs the red part and reflects back the green to look its normal colour.

Grass hit by a yellow sodium light (true yellow) looks black or grey.

See 'An Early Start to Science' (page 19) for more work with coloured filters.

Mixing paint

Children often mix colours when painting. It is a useful scientific exercise to make a systematic record of some of the different permutations and then analyse the results.

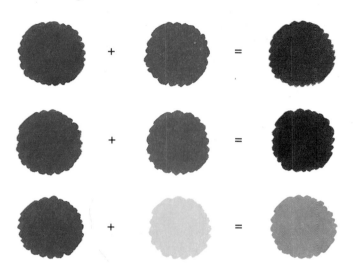

Make sure you try a wide range of colour mixes.

'An Early Start to Science' (pages 20-21) contains further work on colour mixing with pigments and colour mixing by spinning tops.

Look around the classroom and the school for colour. Make up a chart to fill in the things of each colour that you find.

Red	Orange	Yellow	Green	Blue

Purple	Brown	Black	White	Turquoise

Flags

Here are two well-known flags.

The bold colours stand out well.

Design a school flag. Let different groups of children make their own designs. Colour them boldly.

Test them out in the playground. Which designs and colours show up best? Give a score out of ten for each of:
 how well the colour design travels
 the aesthetic quality of the flag.

Diluting colours

Fill a tumbler with water. Add ten drops of food colouring and stir.

Pour half of this coloured liquid into a second tumbler. Add water to the second tumbler to fill it. Repeat the process again.

Go on doing this – diluting the colour further each time.

How many times can you dilute the liquid and still see colour?

Add a secret number of coloured drops to a tumbler of water. Can children match it and find out how many drops you added?

Try diluting orange squash. What is the weakest solution you can see? What is the weakest solution you can taste?

Changing colour

Chop up some red cabbage.

Put it in a saucepan with some water.

Boil it for 5 minutes.

Strain the liquid. It will be a deep blue colour.

Use a medicine dropper to add a few drops of this blue liquid to a variety of other liquids.

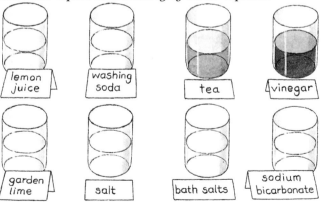

lemon juice | washing soda | tea | vinegar

garden lime | salt | bath salts | sodium bicarbonate

You could try milk, acid drops and cleaning powder as well. Where necessary make the powders and the solids into a solution.

The cabbage water does not keep and will become very smelly!

Red-cabbage water can be used as an indicator. It will turn red, purple, blue or green, as if by magic, depending on which liquid it is added to. You can get a similar effect with a beetroot or blackberry solution. Reds and purples tend to indicate an acid (sour) solution. Blues and greens indicate an alkaline (sweet) solution.

Indicators are often used in chemistry. Litmus (which comes from a lichen) is a well-known example.

Soil-testing kits can be bought from garden centres. These show whether a soil is acid (sour) or alkaline (sweet). By adding lime you can reduce the acidity of the soil.

Colour and density

Mix different amounts of salt with water. Make each solution a different colour using food dyes.

10 tbspn salt | 5 tbspn salt | 2½ tbspn salt | plain water

Put a little of each solution in separate glasses. Very, very carefully add drops of colour from one glass to another. Some will float. Some will sink.

Can children put the liquids in an order? Can anyone layer all the liquids in a glass?

Chromatography

A useful technique for separating differently coloured materials is chromatography. You can use it to find out what pigments felt-tip pen manufacturers use to make various colours, or what colours are present in the sugar coating of Smarties or in food colourings .

There are lots of different ways of doing this.

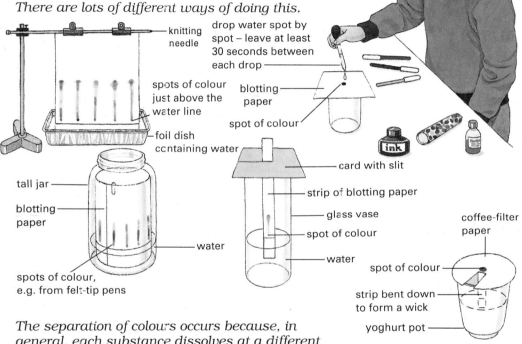

- knitting needle
- drop water spot by spot – leave at least 30 seconds between each drop
- spots of colour just above the water line
- blotting paper
- spot of colour
- foil dish containing water
- card with slit
- tall jar
- blotting paper
- strip of blotting paper
- glass vase
- spot of colour
- water
- water
- spots of colour, e.g. from felt-tip pens
- coffee-filter paper
- spot of colour
- strip bent down to form a wick
- yoghurt pot
- spot of colour
- pipe-cleaner wick
- spot of colour
- wick made from twisted paper

The separation of colours occurs because, in general, each substance dissolves at a different rate. For example, granular sugar dissolves more quickly than demerara sugar.

Small particles of pigment will dissolve quickly and travel away first on the water front. Large particles dissolve more slowly and therefore travel and separate out more slowly. It is thus possible to identify the different pigments used to make up one colour.

Some felt-tip pens are spirit-based and these will not separate with water, they need other solvents.

Colour is helpful. It is used in signs to warn us of danger. It helps us when we are travelling. For example, the underground lines are colour coded. It helps us to differentiate competing sports teams. It helps us to wire a plug correctly, and so on.

Can colour help us to sort things?

Make up a sorting test. Time people to find out how quickly they can match the coloured squares on the grid.

Do people sort letters more quickly?

Does it help if the letters are coloured?

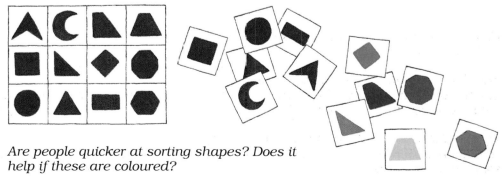

Are people quicker at sorting shapes? Does it help if these are coloured?

A popular starting point for this topic is to consider how we keep ourselves and other things warm. In 'An Early Start to Technology', the section on keeping things warm (pages 62-63) looks at the effects different materials and methods of insulation have on keeping things warm. However, there are other factors, such as the chilling effect from the wind which can be investigated.

Wind chill

An anorak helps protect us from wet, cold <u>and</u> wind.

To demonstrate the wind-chill effect, soak two handkerchiefs in warm water.

Wring out the handkerchiefs. Wrap each hand in a warm damp handkerchief.

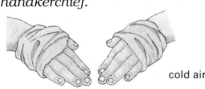

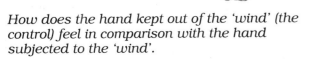

cold air

Hold one hand in front of a hairdryer blowing <u>cold</u> air.

How does the hand kept out of the 'wind' (the control) feel in comparison with the hand subjected to the 'wind'.

Colour and warmth

Another factor in the ability of clothes to keep us warm or cool is their colour. In summer, not only do we wear lightweight clothes like T-shirts, short-sleeved dresses and shorts but we also wear clothes which are light in colour.

Get two children, one wearing a black top and the other a white top, to work sitting in front of a sunny window. Ask them to describe how they feel after a while.

A more formal test is to place two thermometers on a sunlit table and to cover each with a square of material. Use material of the same type and thickness: one piece should be black and the other white. Felt squares are ideal.

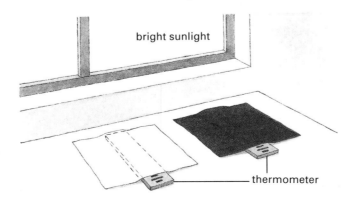

bright sunlight

thermometer

Such work can lead to discussion of the kinds of clothes we need for hot weather. You could look at the different kinds of head protection used against the Sun.

Judging temperature

We are poor judges of temperature as the following experiment shows.

Fill three washing-up bowls with water. Put very warm water in one, tepid water in the second and ice-cold water in the third.

very warm water   tepid water   ice-cold water

Put one hand in the very warm water and the other in the ice-cold water. Leave them there for at least 3 minutes. Then transfer both hands simultaneously to the tepid water.

The hand from the very warm water will feel colder, while the hand from the ice-cold water will feel warmer – even though both hands are in water of the same temperature. This will demonstrate the need for an instrument to measure temperature – the thermometer.

For work using a thermometer in the classroom see 'An Early Start to the Environment' (pages 50-51).

For work on measuring body temperature see 'An Early Start to Ourselves and Evolution' (page 17).

Some facts

There are three states of matter - solid, liquid and gas.

A solid has a definite volume and shape. A liquid has a definite volume, but takes up the shape of its container. A gas has neither a definite volume nor a definite shape.

In a solid, the molecules can vibrate but cannot move from their basic position. They are tightly packed together.

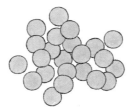

In a liquid, the molecules are free to move around, but are still fairly tightly packed together.

In a gas, the molecules are a long way apart and are free to move around.

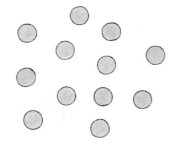

Most substances can exist in all three states. Ice, liquid water and steam is a familiar example of this. It is comparatively easy to change water from gas (steam) to liquid to solid (ice).

True steam is invisible. Look at the clear zone next to the spout of a boiling kettle. After a few centimetres it begins to condense to visible water vapour.

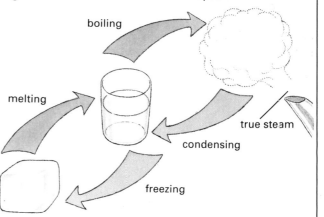

When heat energy is applied to an ice block, the molecules gain sufficient energy to overcome the forces holding them in position and a liquid is formed. Similarly, if sufficient heat is applied to the liquid water, the molecules gain enough energy to move much further apart and escape through the surface to form a gas (steam). Conversely, energy must be removed (cooling) to change the steam back to liquid water and subsequently to ice.

The energy required to change a substance from one state to another is called latent (hidden) heat.

In pure substances these changes in state take place at definite temperatures. Ice begins to melt at 0°C when heat is applied to it. Similarly, liquid water turns to ice at 0°C when heat is removed from it. Melting and freezing both happen at the melting or freezing point (both terms are used).

Convection in gases

In solids the molecules can vibrate but they cannot move about. In a gas, the molecules can move about. Warm air above a radiator rises because as it warms up it expands. Since the same amount of air now takes up a bigger volume its density becomes less, and so it rises to float on denser cooler air. This movement is called a convection current.

Gliders and birds use the convection currents to glide higher and higher on what are called thermals.

Make a spinning snake

It is easy to demonstrate convection currents in gases to the children.

1 Cut a spiral from thin card or paper to make a snake.

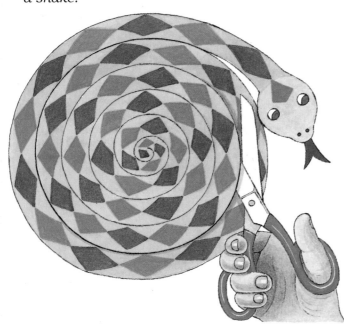

2 *Thread cotton through the end of the snake's tail.*

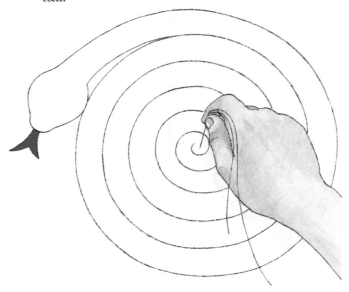

3 *Dangle the snake from a thread above a lamp or radiator.*

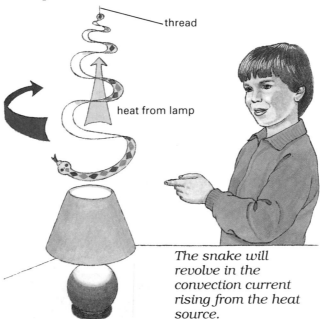

thread

heat from lamp

The snake will revolve in the convection current rising from the heat source.

Other spinners

Another spinner can easily be made from a milk bottle top.

1 *Flatten out a milk bottle top.*

2 *Push up a small bump in the centre of the top with the rounded lid of a ball-point pen. Cut and twist fins.*

3 *Balance the top on a needle set in a cork. Position the set-up over a heat source.*

Another type of spinner can be made from a metal foil dish, the kind used for baking cakes. Cut the vanes carefully with a craft knife. Set it on a pencil stuck in a cotton reel above a heat source.

Convection in liquids

If you heat water, it expands and the water molecules move apart. This water becomes less dense, and so rises to float above the colder, denser water, thus you have a convection current.

Convection in action

You can easily demonstrate convection with a large aquarium and a disused ink bottle.

Fill the ink bottle with hot water, coloured with ink. Screw the top on and place it at the bottom of a tank full of <u>cold</u> water. Very gently remove the top from the bottle.

The coloured hot water slowly rises and circulates in the tank. The colour enables you see what is happening.

Convection currents in everyday use

Convection currents carry the heat around a domestic hot-water system.

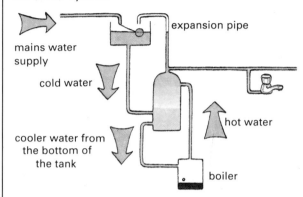

The ice box at the top of a fridge cools the air down. It becomes denser and falls. Less dense air at the base of the fridge (it is very slightly warmer) rises to replace the cold air.

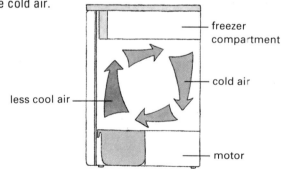

Gliders rise on convection currents, called thermals.

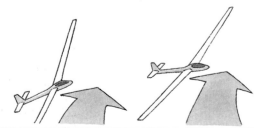

Gulls use convection currents to gain height.

Sea and land breezes

During the day the land heats up more quickly than the sea. (It has a lower specific heat capacity.) The land heats the air above it so that the air starts to rise as it gets less dense. The air above the sea remains cool and dense.

As the hot air on the land rises so that cool air over the sea moves in to take its place. Thus, we have a sea breeze coming in-shore.

During the night, the land cools more quickly than the sea. The air above the sea is now warmer than that above the land. The air above the sea rises and the cooler air from the land flows to take its place. Thus, we have a land breeze going off-shore.

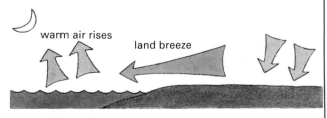

Conduction in solids

Collect some long thin objects made of various materials. Stand them in a jug of hot water, with one end sticking out.

Feel the tops of the objects. Which conducts (passes heat along) the best?

Keep a record.

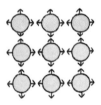

wooden spoon
glass rod
plastic spoon
long nail
rubber tubing
metal spoon

Material	Result
wooden spoon	poor conductor
metal spoon	good conductor

How does conduction work?

The molecules which make up a solid are close together. When one end of an object is placed in hot water, the molecules gain kinetic energy. That is to say, they move faster. (Of course this movement is so small that you cannot see it.) The extra movement affects other molecules nearby and makes them move more. They in turn affect ones near them and so on. This is <u>conduction</u> of heat energy.

Solids such as metals are good conductors of heat energy because the molecules in a metal can move easily. Solids such as plastics have complicated molecules which cannot move easily; heat energy travels slowly through them. They are good insulators.

Make a display of good conductors and good insulators.

Conduction in liquids and gases

Why are liquids and gases not good conductors?

In liquids and gases, atoms and molecules have no regular arrangement, therefore heat passes from one molecule to another more slowly than in a solid. Water is a poor conductor of heat when compared with solids. Gases are even poorer conductors.

Air is an excellent insulating material. Trapped in wool fibres, in cork or in expanded polystyrene, it is often used as an insulator.

Investigate the effect of a layer of trapped air on the cooling rate of water.

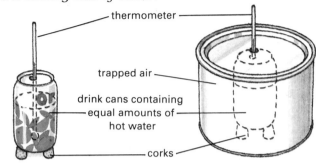

thermometer

trapped air

drink cans containing equal amounts of hot water

corks

Record the drop in temperature every 15 minutes. How do the two cans compare after 2 hours?

Compare different insulators by finding out how fast the water cools down.

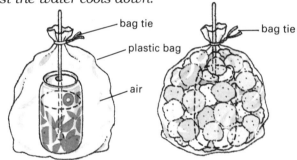

bag tie

bag tie

plastic bag

air

control   *loose cotton wool*

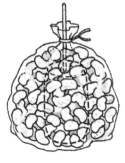 

polystyrene chips   *feathers or cork chips*

We have seen that when any material, be it a solid, liquid or a gas, gains heat energy that its molecules move more. This causes the material to expand. Expansion in solids is not easy to see.

These activities will make this expansion apparent.

Expanding wire

copper wire

string

brick almost touching the floor

Heat the copper wire with the candle. Does the copper expand enough for the house brick to touch the floor?

Tight fit

Two traditional pieces of equipment available from scientific suppliers that illustrate expansion are the ball and ring, and the bar and gauge.

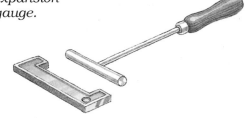

At room temperature, the ball just goes through the ring. When the ball is heated up, it won't go through.

At room temperature, the bar will fit in the gap. When the bar is heated, it won't fit the gap.

Bimetallic strips

Some metals expand more than others. In a bimetallic strip, two metals are joined together. When the strip is heated, one metal expands more than the other and the strip bends.

You can buy bimetallic strip from a scientific supplier. You can use it to make a fire alarm.

brass brass

cold iron hot iron

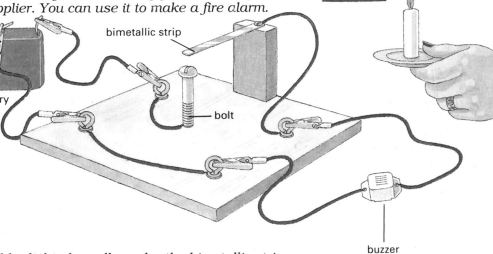

bimetallic strip

4.5V battery

bolt

buzzer

Hold a lighted candle under the bimetallic strip. You will have to experiment to make sure that when the strip is heated, it will curve downwards. If not, then turn it over.

Sticking drawers

Drawers often stick. Is this due to heating?

Cut four pegs from dowel rod. Drill four holes for the pegs in a block of wood. Make sure they are a tight fit.

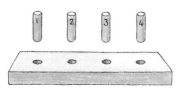

Keep one peg in the classroom as a control.

Put one in a refrigerator for an hour.

Put one in a warm oven for an hour.

Do they still fit in the block?

Leave the fourth peg hanging in a damp atmosphere overnight.

Try it in its hole the next day.

Why do you think drawers stick?

Expansion of air

Fit the end of a balloon tightly over the spout of an empty 5 litre oil can. Leave the can on a sunny windowsill or over a radiator.

Watch the balloon expand as the temperature rises.

Put a balloon over the end of an empty sauce bottle. Stand the bottle in hot water and leave.

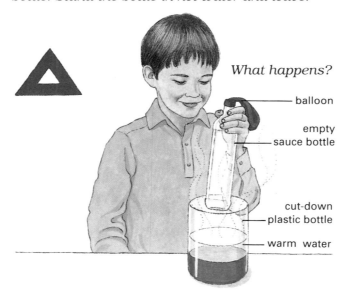

What happens?

- balloon
- empty sauce bottle
- cut-down plastic bottle
- warm water

Expansion of liquids

Liquid expansion is used in a thermometer.

1 *Fill a small drinks bottle with water.*

2 *Insert a plastic drinking straw into the bottle.*

3 *Secure the straw in place with Plasticine to make an airtight seal.*

Plasticine

4 *Stand the bottle in a cut-down 3 litre plastic lemonade bottle. Pour warm water around it.*

What happens?

What is radiant heat?

We can often feel the heat coming directly from an object. Such heat is coming to us by radiation. As it travels at the same speed as light, it appears to reach us instantaneously.

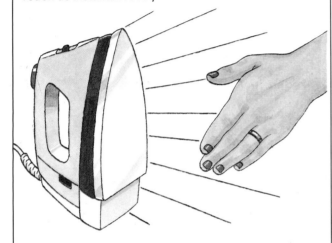

All objects give out rays of heat energy, but we do not notice them unless the object is really hot. These rays are infra-red radiation. The Sun, which of course is extremely hot, gives out a lot of infra-red radiation. This radiation takes about 8 minutes to travel the 150 million kilometres from the Sun to the Earth.

Radiation is direct. It comes straight from its source and it does not, like conduction, need molecules to pass on the energy, or as in convection (see pages 38-39) need the movement of molecules. It can travel through a vacuum and does so to reach us from the Sun.

An electric bar fire hardly heats up the air in a room; you need to be near it in order to <u>absorb</u> its radiation.

What surfaces absorb radiant heat best?

Find two identical empty drinks cans. Paint one black and the other silver.

Put the same amount of water and a thermometer in each. Stand them in front of a radiant heat source.

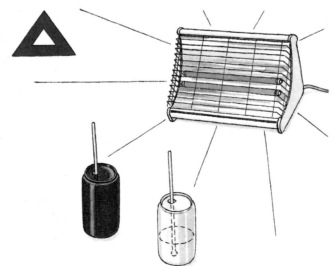

Take the temperature of the water in each can at five-minute intervals after switching on the radiant heat source.

Plot two graphs showing how the temperature of the water in each can changes.

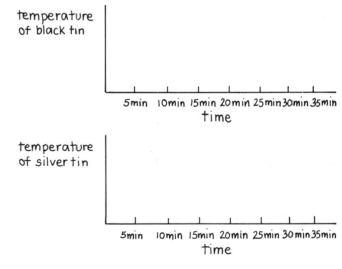

The black can is a good absorber of heat and the shiny silver can is a poor absorber of heat. This is the reason why it is best to have a teapot with a shiny, rather than dull and dirty, inside.

A good way to begin work on the topic of sound is by collecting sounds around you, both indoors and out. 'An Early Start to the Environment' (pages 20-21) and 'An Early Start to Ourselves and Evolution' (pages 33-35) describe the sort of activities that can be pursued.

Try to classify the sounds you collect.

Loud	Soft
shouting	whispering
thunder	rustling leaves
clapping	lullabies

Pleasant	Unpleasant
piano playing	car horn blowing
birds singing	loud radios
laughing	crying

Try to describe the sounds in words. This is difficult to do, but leads to an appreciation of the quality of sounds. For example, what is the difference between, 'crackles', 'squeaks' and 'rustles'.

Find words that resemble the sound they describe; for example, 'crash', 'swish', 'splash', 'buzz', 'crunch' and 'hiss'.

Find out how different animals make sounds. Try to imitate their sounds.

The vibrations of fast beating wings make the sound of a bee.

A frog blows air from internal vocal sacs.

Try beating your chest!

Dogs have vibrating vocal cords like humans.

Owls use the voice call 'Too-whit, too-whoo.'

A cricket rubs its hind legs together.

Making sounds

Investigate the different ways in which you can make sounds in the classroom. Use pencils, rulers, jars, boxes, cubes, radiators, keys and so on.

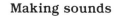

Tapping rhythms

Tap on a table top with a pencil or a ruler. Tap out the rhythm of a nursery rhyme. Can others guess what it is? Try doing the same for pop-songs.

Vibrations

Sound is caused by vibrations. When we hit, pluck, bow, or rub objects, we often make a sound. Children need to experiment with different ways of making sound in order to try to determine what is causing it.

Pluck a rubber band stretched over a plastic box. Watch it as you let go.

Pluck a ruler sticking out from a table.

Blow across the top of a bottle. (This sets the air inside vibrating.)

Tap a bottle. (This sets the glass vibrating.)

Whirl a ruler securely tied on a string above your head.

tie string through a hole made at the end of the ruler

Blow between two pieces of paper held between your hands.

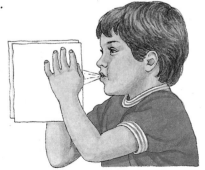

Feel your Adam's apple as you talk.

Sprinkle some seeds on a drum top. Tap the drum skin. What happens?

Tap a suspended ping-pong ball with a vibrating tuning fork.

Set a springboard in motion at the swimming baths.

Collect together different kinds of musical instrument from around the school. Try to classify them.

Look for pictures of musical instruments. Try sorting and separating them too. You will find some fall into more than one category .

Instruments played by hitting or shaking

Instruments played by blowing

Instruments played by plucking

Instruments played by rubbing (or bowing)

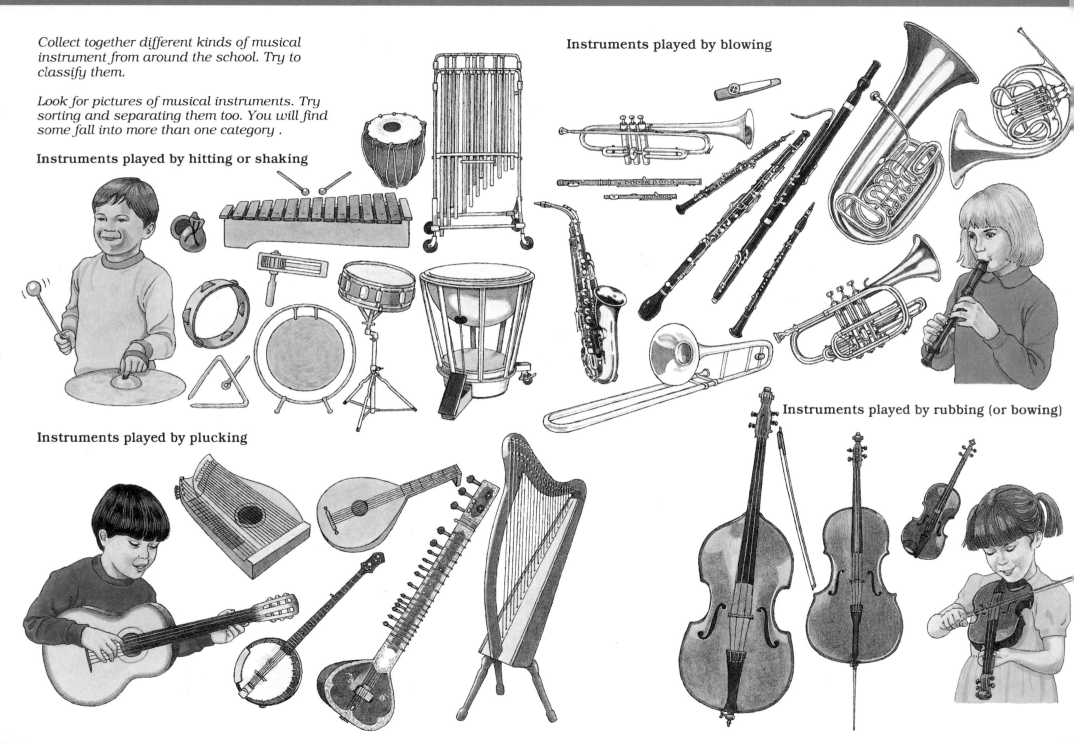

'The Young Person's Guide to the Orchestra' by Benjamin Britten is a good introduction to the instruments of the orchestra.

Here are some other suggestions for highlighting individual instruments.

Cello:
'The Swan' from
'Carnival of the Animals'
(Saint-Saëns)

Double bass:
'The Elephant' from
'Carnival of the Animals'
(Saint Saëns)

Horn:
'Evening Prayer' from
'Hansel and Gretel'
(Humperdinck)

Trumpet
'Trumpet Concerto'
(Haydn)

Oboe:
'Jesu, Joy of Man's Desiring'
(Bach)

Xylophone
'Fossils' from
'Carnival of the Animals'
(Saint-Saëns)

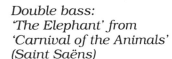

Make a plastic-bottle banjo

You will need a piece of wood, a large plastic bottle, some nylon fishing line, seven screw eyes, a nail, a small piece of wood to form a bridge and a craft knife.

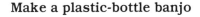
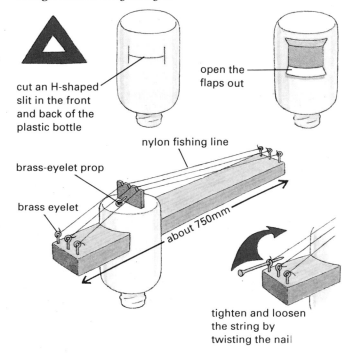

cut an H-shaped slit in the front and back of the plastic bottle

open the flaps out

nylon fishing line

brass-eyelet prop

brass eyelet

about 750mm

tighten and loosen the string by twisting the nail

Make a paper-straw whistle

1 Take a drinking straw (the waxed paper ones are best).

2 Flatten one end for about 2 cm.

3 Trim off the corners of the flattened end.

4 Put the flat end in your mouth, just above your tongue, and blow.

What happens to the note if you make a straw shorter?

Make a hose-pipe horn

Any length of hose pipe will do. Put a tap connector at one end and insert a plastic funnel securely at the other.

tap connector

funnel

Press your lips firmly together. Blow out strongly.

The pitch of the sound depends on how firmly your lips are compressed together and on the length of the tube.

See 'An Early Start to Science' (pages 10-12) and 'An Early Start to Technology' (page 61) for more instruments to make.

Sound travels through solids, liquids and gases. Activities to show this are found in 'An Early Start to Science' (page 13), 'An Early Start to the Environment' (pages 20-21) and 'An Early Start to Ourselves and Evolution' (pages 34-35).

What is the nature of sound waves and how do they travel through different media?

There are two kinds of wave motion: transverse waves and longitudinal waves. The children will be much more familiar with the first of these even though <u>sound waves are longitudinal waves</u>.

Do some simple demonstrations to illustrate these two kinds of waves.

What are transverse waves?

Fix one end of an 8 metre length of rope to a suitable upright such as a railing or a netball post. Move the free end up and down.

A wave will travel along the rope to the railing and back again. Any one part of the rope moves just <u>up and down</u>, yet the wave appears to travel along the rope. This is a transverse wave.

Half fill a washing-up bowl with water. Float a small object on the surface of the water. Drop a pebble into the centre of the bowl.

This sets up waves which travel outward. These are again transverse waves. The water particles (as shown by the float) move just <u>up and down</u>, but the wave moves outwards at right angles to the particles.

What are longitudinal waves?

Secure one end of a piece of catapult or knicker elastic to some railings. Ask a child (A) to hold the other end of the elastic taut. Get a second child (B) to rest a hand on the elastic and a third child (C) to gently tug the elastic and immediately release it.

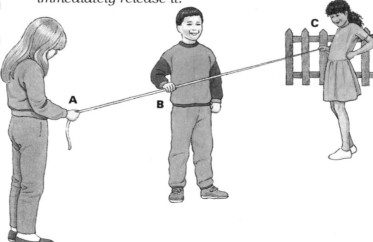

The elastic does not move, but child B will clearly feel the tug. The direction of disturbance of the elastic and the direction of the wave are the same. This is a longitudinal wave.

You can also use a Slinky to demonstrate longitudinal waves.

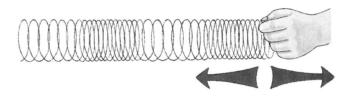

Here the horizontal movement generates a longitudinal wave.

Words used to describe waves

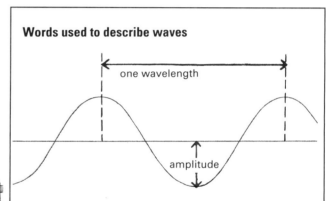

The <u>wavelength</u> is the distance between two peaks or troughs.

<u>Amplitude</u> is the height of the wave (plucking the rope more vigorously gives higher waves, that is a greater amplitude).

<u>Frequency</u>: if the speed of the up and down disturbance of the rope changes, the speed with which the wave travels along the rope – its frequency – is changed. The frequency is the number of complete waves per second. The unit of measurement is hertz (Hz). Frequencies of fast vibrations are given in kilohertz (kHz).

Sound waves are a form of energy. They are a special kind of kinetic energy due to the movement of molecules in air. When a vibration, of say a drum, is set up, it causes the molecules of air near it to vibrate. These cause the molecules next to them to vibrate. These in turn set up vibrations in molecules next to them and so on. In this way the sound is carried through the air.

Air can be compressed

Hold a finger over the end of a bicycle pump as you push the handle down. If you let go of the handle, it springs back. The compressed air pushes it up.

Flap a door to and fro. Do papers blow off the desk and tables? Do the curtains flutter?

Newton's cradle

It is difficult for children to understand that the air molecules do not move along with the sound but merely pass on the energy of their movement. The following demonstration with a Newton's cradle is very illuminating.

The end ball is pulled out at an angle and then released. Its energy is transferred from ball to ball, until the ball at the far end flies out.

If you don't have a Newton's cradle, you can simulate its action by using a folded piece of card as a trough and some marbles.

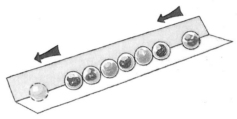

Sound can be reflected

Shout into a bucket – a metal one is best. The bottom of the bucket reflects the sound back. This is added to the original shout, so making it louder.

An echo is a sound reflection. You can use echoes to work out the speed of sound (see 'An Early Start to the Environment', page 21)

The pitch of a note, that is its highness or lowness, depends on the speed of the vibrations, that is their frequency.

Make a buzz saw

Use the shape on the right as a template to make a toothed wheel from card. Punch two holes either side of the centre as shown. Thread a metre of thin string through the holes and tie the ends together.

Loop the string over your fingers. Pull the string outwards and relax. Keep repeating this to make the wheel spin.

Hold the spinning disc against a sheet of paper sticking out from the table as shown to obtain a buzzing noise.

Vary the speed of the vibrations by varying the speed at which the disc rotates. The rise and fall of the note will be evident. How does the pitch vary with speed of spinning?

Some more vibrations

Run a finger nail slowly along the teeth of a comb. Listen to the scraping noise you get.

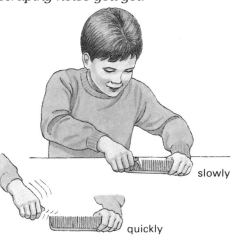

slowly

quickly

Now do it quickly. The faster the movement, the higher the noise.

Run a ruler along some railings.

Run a pencil across corrugated card. Listen to how the note goes up as the speed increases.

Vibrate a ruler sticking out from the edge of a table. The less ruler which sticks out, the higher the speed of vibration and the higher the note.

Make notes with a bicycle

Turn a bicycle upside down. Slowly revolve the back wheel by turning the pedals. Hold a piece of card against the spokes of the back wheel as it spins. You will get a series of separate sounds.

It is best for the teacher to hold the card, rather than risk a child catching his or her fingers in the spokes.

Gradually increase the speed of the wheel to show that you can get a continuous note. The faster the wheel turns, the higher the pitch of the sound.

Also try holding the card against the spinning tyre.

Look at other factors affecting pitch

Compare the vibrations from a long length of line with those from a short length.

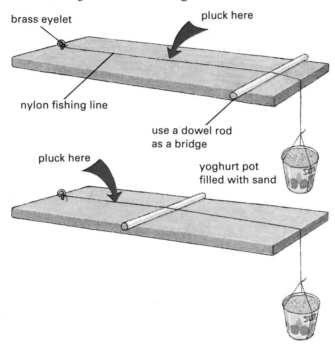

brass eyelet

pluck here

nylon fishing line

use a dowel rod as a bridge

pluck here

yoghurt pot filled with sand

The shorter the line, the higher the notes.

Now increase the amount of sand so that the line is pulled much tighter.

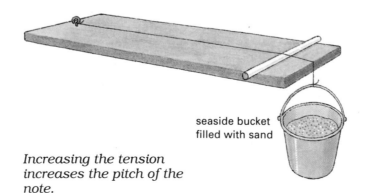

seaside bucket filled with sand

Increasing the tension increases the pitch of the note.

Compare thick string with thin string.

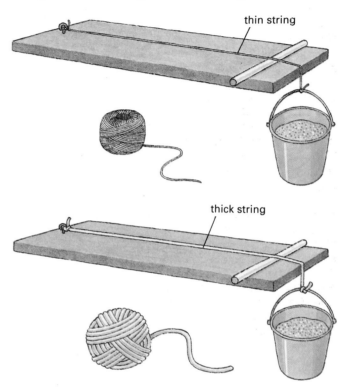

thin string

thick string

The thinner the string the higher the pitch.

Try using a metal guitar string. How does it compare with string and nylon fishing line?

The difference in pitch needs a keen ear, but the denser the material, the lower the pitch.

Summary

The shorter the line <u>or</u>
the greater the tension <u>or</u>
the thinner the line <u>or</u>
the less dense the line,
<u>then</u> the higher the note (that is, the greater the number of vibrations per second).

Make a water trombone

You will need a long thin tube (for example a piece of garden hose, plastic tubing or copper tube) and a bottle almost filled with water.

Blow across the top of the tube as you raise and lower it in the bottle.

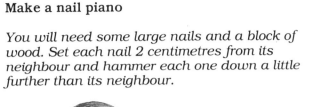

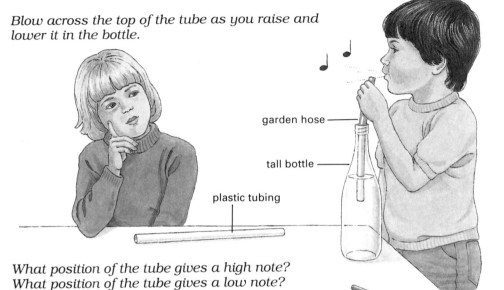

garden hose

tall bottle

plastic tubing

copper piping

What position of the tube gives a high note?
What position of the tube gives a low note?

Try different widths of tube.

In all cases the sound is caused by the vibrating column of air in the tube.

How does a great organ work?

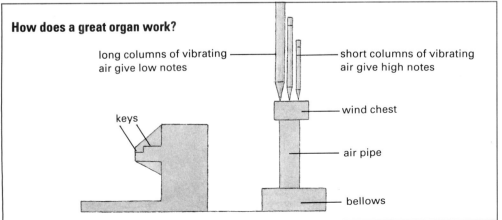

long columns of vibrating air give low notes

short columns of vibrating air give high notes

wind chest

keys

air pipe

bellows

Make a nail piano

You will need some large nails and a block of wood. Set each nail 2 centimetres from its neighbour and hammer each one down a little further than its neighbour.

Hit each of the nails with a spare large nail. The shorter the nail being hit, the higher will be the note.

Stick a coloured tab of paper in front of each nail. Ask the children to make up tunes and write the score in colour.

How does a grand piano work?

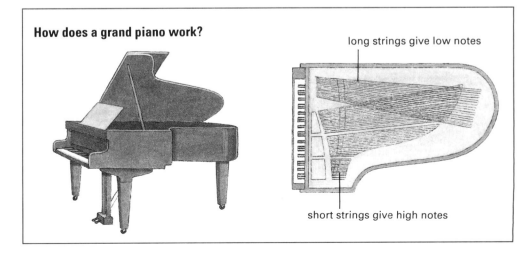

long strings give low notes

short strings give high notes

Some facts about pitch

piano keyboard

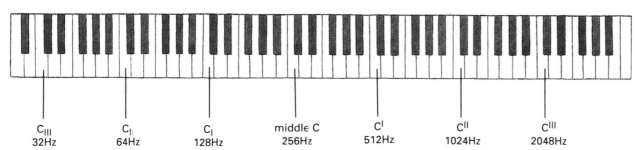

C_{III}	C_{II}	C_I	middle C	C^I	C^{II}	C^{III}
32Hz	64Hz	128Hz	256Hz	512Hz	1024Hz	2048Hz

Middle C has a frequency of 256 Hz. This pitch is produced by anything that vibrates 256 times per second. C^I is an octave above. It has double the number of vibrations per second, that is 512. C_I is an octave below. It has half the number of vibrations per second, that is 128.

Sound waves can be displayed on an oscilloscope. Here are the frequencies of two different notes.

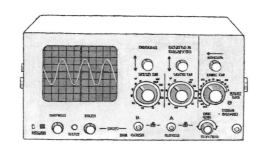

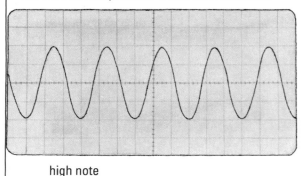

high note

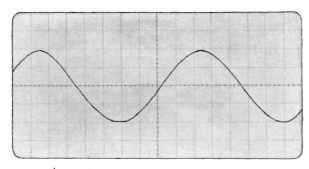

low note

A high note with its greater frequency has the peaks and troughs of its wave pattern closer together than a low note.

Summary

Pitch depends on the frequency of vibration of an object. It can be altered by:
- altering the length, tension or material of a string

or
- changing the length of a vibrating column of air.

Loudness depends on the size of the vibrations. The bigger the vibration, the louder the sound.

Hit a drum gently. Hit a drum hard. The bigger the vibration of the drum skin, the louder the sound. So, the harder you hit the drum (that is to say, the more energy you use), the louder the sound.

Pluck a guitar string gently. Pluck a guitar string strongly. Which sound is the louder?

Blow into a recorder. What is the difference between how you make a loud sound and a quiet sound?

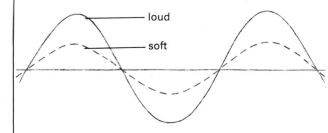

On an oscilloscope two notes of the same pitch, but one loud and the other soft, look like this.

— loud

— soft

The height of the vibration, the amplitude, is larger for the louder sound.

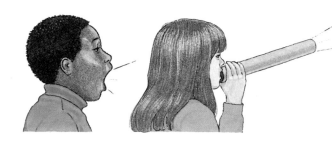

Other factors affecting loudness

The distance you are from the sound affects how well you can hear it.

Stand on the opposite side of the playground or school field to a child holding a quietly playing transistor radio. As you come closer, what happens?

The sound energy is travelling out from its source. It dissipates itself as it spreads. The air molecules near the listeners are vibrating much less than those near the radio.

Directing the sound affects how well you hear it. Shout at the rest of the class across the school playground. Now shout at them through a long cardboard tube.

The tube acts like a megaphone – directing the sounds to the listeners, and making it louder than it would otherwise have been.

A bandstand roof directs the sounds out to the listening audience.

How can you increase the volume?

Increasing the volume of vibrating air increases the volume of the sound.

Place a vibrating tuning fork on a wooden table. Then put it on top of a wooden box. Compare the volume of the two sounds.

wooden box

When the fork is put on the box, the air inside it vibrates. This increases the amount of vibrating air, and so the sound becomes louder.

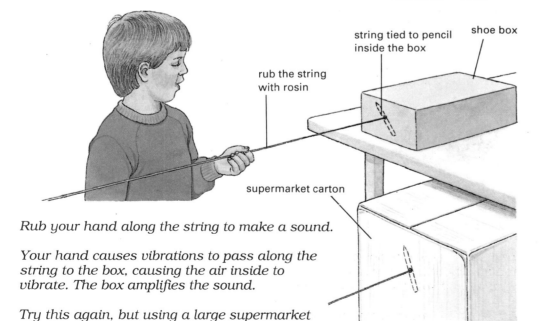

string tied to pencil inside the box

shoe box

rub the string with rosin

supermarket carton

Rub your hand along the string to make a sound.

Your hand causes vibrations to pass along the string to the box, causing the air inside to vibrate. The box amplifies the sound.

Try this again, but using a large supermarket carton.

How does a piano work?

Ask a child to strike a note, first softly and then sharply. The harder the key is struck, the louder the note.

sustaining pedal

Take the front off the piano. Look at the hammers which strike the strings and the dampers which hold the strings still.

When a hammer strikes a string, the damper is released, so that the string can vibrate. It will go on vibrating until it comes to rest or until the key is released, which immediately brings the damper back onto the string.

Depress the right-hand pedal – the sustaining pedal. This lifts the dampers away from the strings so that the strings can go on vibrating even when the key is released.

With the sustaining pedal pressed down, ask the children to sing into the piano. Those strings that have the same frequency as the sounds made by the children, vibrate back. This is called resonance.

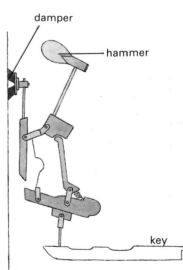

damper

hammer

key

string

Light waves, X-rays and so on belong to a family of waves called electromagnetic waves. The chart below shows where they fit into the electromagnetic spectrum. They are all produced by the movement of electrons in materials.

wavelength (normally measured in metres)

wavelength increasing

Radio waves and microwaves	Infra-red	Visible light	Ultra-violet	X-rays	Gamma rays
Produced by oscillating electric currents.	Produced by hot objects.	Produced by hot objects. Produced by electrical discharge, e.g. lightning.	Produced by the sun. Produced by electrical discharges, e.g. discharge lamps.	Produced in an X-ray tube.	Produced by radioactive materials.
These have the longest wavelength and the lowest frequency. They are used for radar and to carry radio and TV signals. Microwaves are very short radio waves. They can be used for cooking.	These can be felt as heat. They can be used to trace bacterial infection, because bacteria glow brightly if hit by infra-red rays.	We can see these rays. We call them light. They can be split into the colours of the rainbow: red at one end and violet at the other.	Ultra-violet gives us a sun tan.	X-rays pass through substances such as fat and muscle, but are stopped by bone; so they can be used to look at bone structure.	These are the most penetrating rays. They have the shortest wavelength and the greatest amount of energy. They are harmful to us above a certain level.

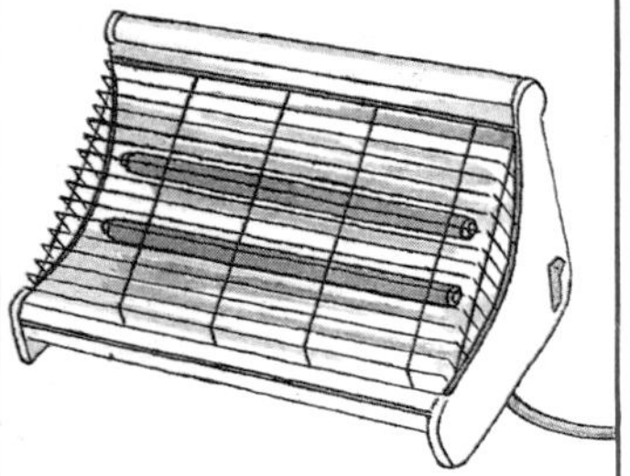

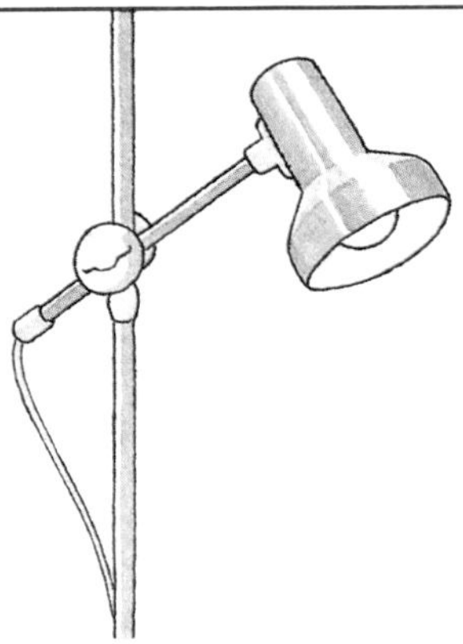

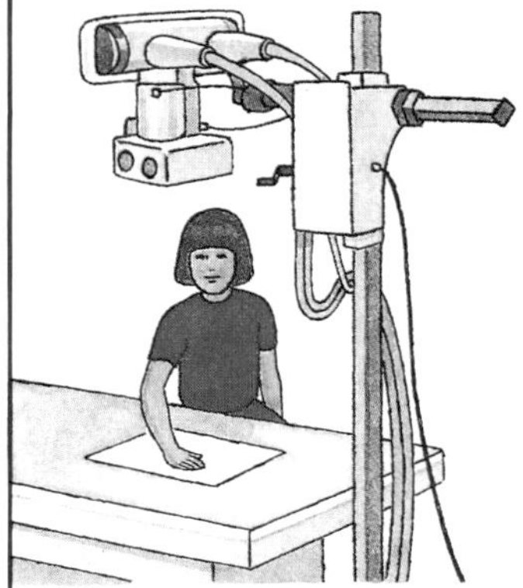

frequency and energy increasing

frequency (normally measured in hertz)

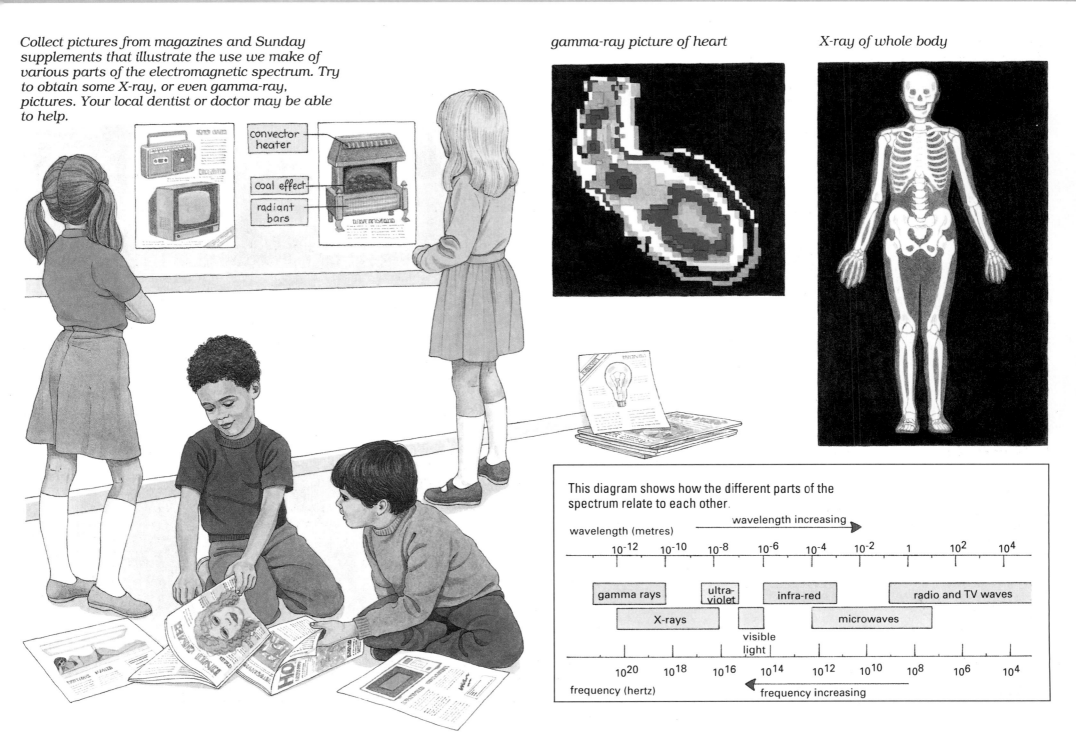

Collect pictures from magazines and Sunday supplements that illustrate the use we make of various parts of the electromagnetic spectrum. Try to obtain some X-ray, or even gamma-ray, pictures. Your local dentist or doctor may be able to help.

convector heater

coal effect

radiant bars

gamma-ray picture of heart

X-ray of whole body

This diagram shows how the different parts of the spectrum relate to each other.

wavelength increasing →

wavelength (metres)

| 10^{-12} | 10^{-10} | 10^{-8} | 10^{-6} | 10^{-4} | 10^{-2} | 1 | 10^{2} | 10^{4} |

gamma rays | ultra-violet | infra-red | radio and TV waves

X-rays | visible light | microwaves

| 10^{20} | 10^{18} | 10^{16} | 10^{14} | 10^{12} | 10^{10} | 10^{8} | 10^{6} | 10^{4} |

frequency (hertz)

← frequency increasing

To study electricity you will need some basic equipment. That shown below will meet most of your needs.

Cells and batteries

4.5 V bell battery

1.5 V

4.5 V torch battery

It is best to choose a standard battery. The activities on the following pages all use 4.5 V bell batteries. They stand up well and the two top terminals are easy to use. Use them in conjunction with a 3.5 V bulb.

Wire

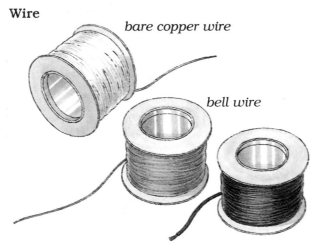

bare copper wire

bell wire

Extra-flexible wire (available from RS Components) is very convenient for use by children as it doesn't kink.

Bulbs

2.5 V   3.5 V   bulb holders

Other equipment

galvanometer

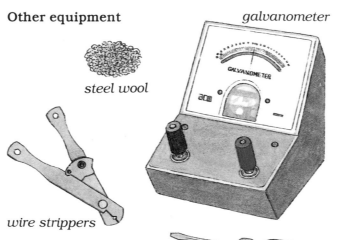

steel wool

wire strippers

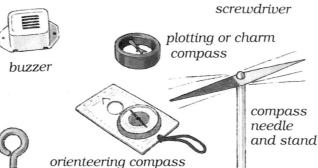

soft iron rods   small screwdriver

buzzer

plotting or charm compass

brass eyelets

orienteering compass

compass needle and stand

small washers   crocodile clips

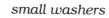

Mount bulb holders

Put the bulb holders on small wooden blocks as this makes them easier to use.

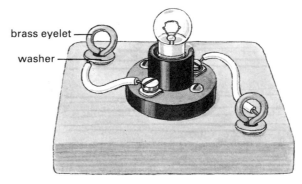

brass eyelet

washer

Make-up connecting wires

Cut 30 cm lengths of extra flexible wire. Bare each end and connect them to crocodile clips.

always put the bare wire end under the screw this way round

tighten

Make switches

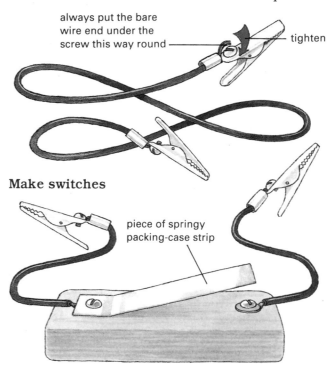

piece of springy packing-case strip

Find out how a torch works

A useful place to begin
investigations into electricity is
with a torch. Make sure that it
works, before you begin!

Take the torch to pieces. The top
will unscrew, exposing the main
case. This will probably hold two
cylindrical cells which can be tipped
out. The top will come to pieces so
that you can remove the bulb.

Let the children play with the
pieces. Can anyone light the bulb
outside the torch? It is useful to
have some spare pieces of wire
with bared ends lying on the table.

It may take some time, but usually
someone eventually finds out how
to light the bulb. Don't rush the
children, for the discovery that to
light the bulb there must be a
<u>continuous metal pathway</u> is a
very important one.

Can anyone put the torch back
together again so that it lights?

The need for a circuit can also be
shown by connecting a bulb in its
bulbholder block to a battery.

bare wire

bare wire

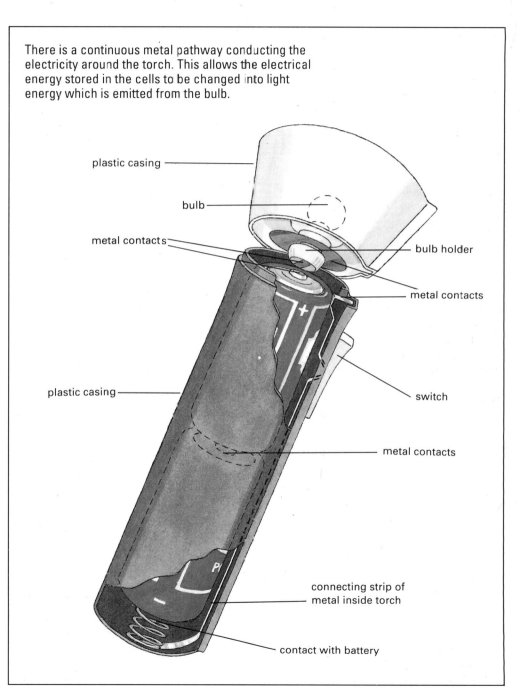

There is a continuous metal pathway conducting the
electricity around the torch. This allows the electrical
energy stored in the cells to be changed into light
energy which is emitted from the bulb.

plastic casing

bulb

metal contacts

bulb holder

metal contacts

plastic casing

switch

metal contacts

connecting strip of
metal inside torch

contact with battery

Break the circuit

How many ways can children find to put the bulb out?

Any break in the continuous metal pathway – the circuit – causes the bulb to go out. Unclipping a crocodile clip will do this, as will unscrewing the bulb. A break in the circuit is equivalent to a switch.

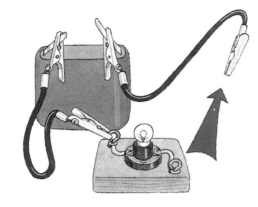

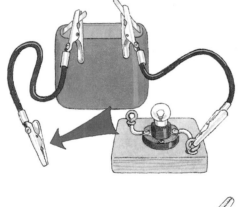

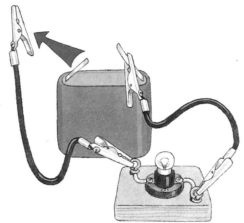

Switches

Put a switch in the circuit.

The springy-metal case strip switch is useful. The light goes off once it is released which saves on batteries!

If you tap the switch, the light will flash on and off.

How is a bulb made?

Remove the glass from a bulb by holding it in a cloth and breaking the glass with a pliers.

very thin wire filament

thicker supporting wires held apart by a glass bead

one wire extends to metal knob at the base of the bulb

wire soldered onto outer case

Painting and drawing

Let the children make large-scale paintings or drawings of a bulb on A4 sheets of paper. Encourage them to look at it in detail. A hand lens will help.

a bulb

Ask the children to make large-scale paintings and drawings of the simple circuits that they make. This will help emphasise the concept of a complete circuit.

a circuit

Make illuminated models

Putting simple circuits in a context where they do a 'real' job of work makes them more meaningful to children.

At a very simple level you can make a 'ceiling light' for a shoe-box room.

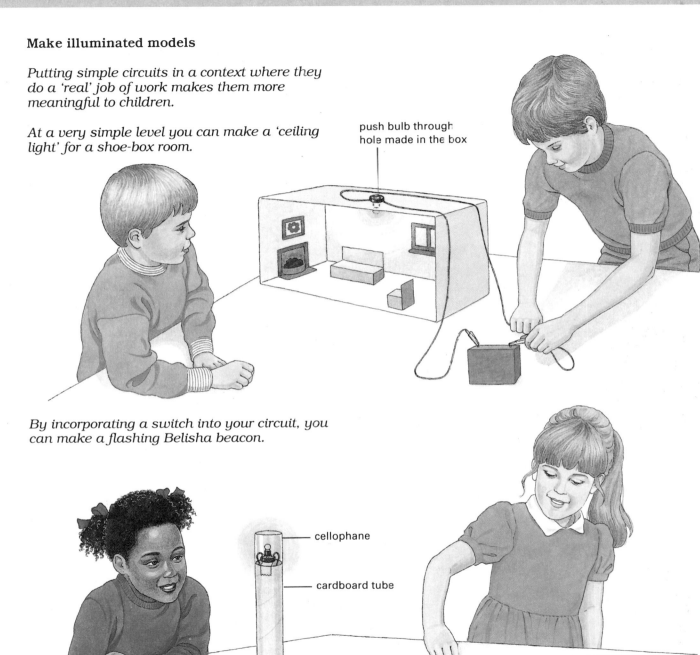

push bulb through hole made in the box

By incorporating a switch into your circuit, you can make a flashing Belisha beacon.

cellophane

cardboard tube

What conducts electricity?

Try various objects across the gap in the circuit to see which conduct electricity and which are insulators.

Keep a record of your results.

Conductors	Insulators
fork	saucer
bracelet	rubber band
key	protractor

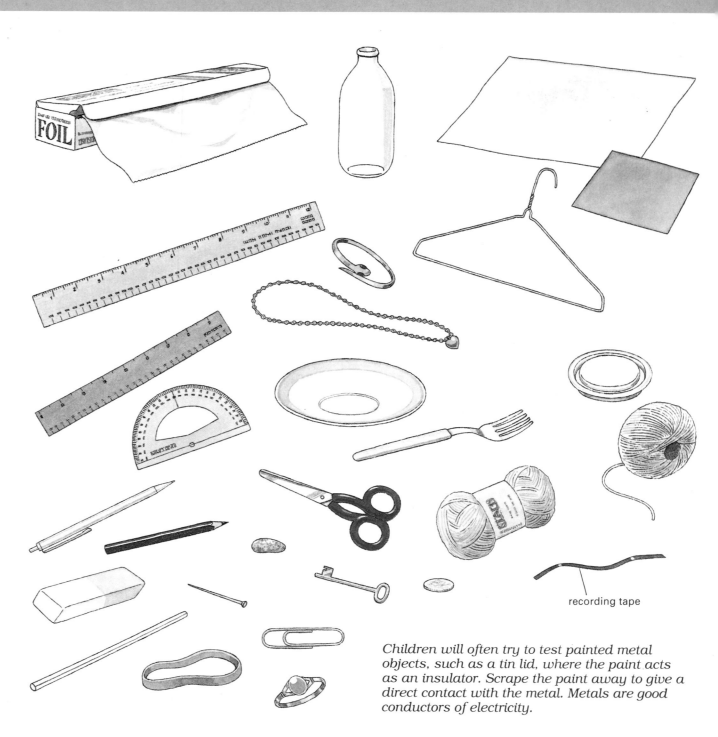

recording tape

Children will often try to test painted metal objects, such as a tin lid, where the paint acts as an insulator. Scrape the paint away to give a direct contact with the metal. Metals are good conductors of electricity.

Connecting bulbs

Let children experiment with different ways of connecting two bulbs.

They usually connect them like this. This is called a _series_ circuit.

Do these two bulbs glow as brightly as when there is only one in the circuit?

As this is a single circuit, any break in it will affect all the bulbs in the circuit.

a series circuit

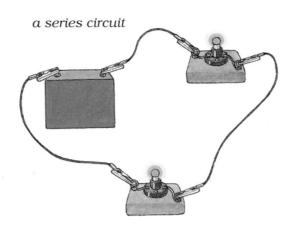

Some children may connect the bulbs like this. This is called a _parallel_ circuit.

How does the brightness of these bulbs compare with that of the bulbs in the series circuit?

Each bulb in this parallel circuit has its own separate circuit. It is not affected if the other bulb is disconnected. Each bulb receives power independently of the other circuit. Each bulb has the same brightness. More power is used than in the two-bulb series circuit, and so the battery will not last as long.

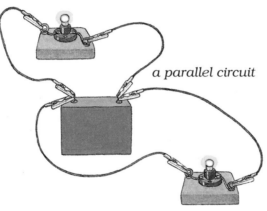

a parallel circuit

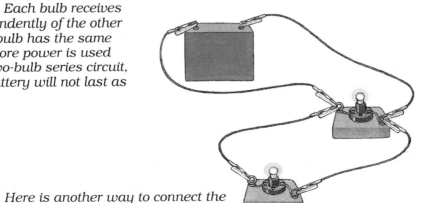

Here is another way to connect the same parallel circuit.

Make some models using two lights

Two 'ceiling lights' connected in series.

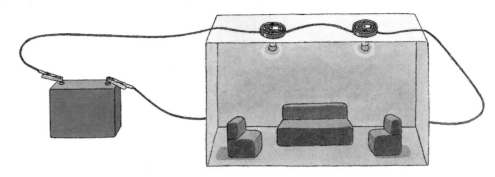

Two 'ceiling lights' connected in parallel.

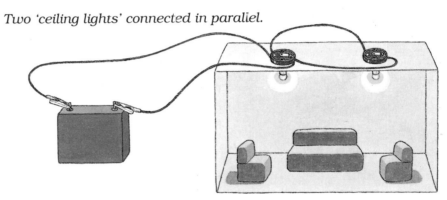

Which system gives the most brightly lit room: series or parallel?

How can you make the eyes shine as brightly as possible?

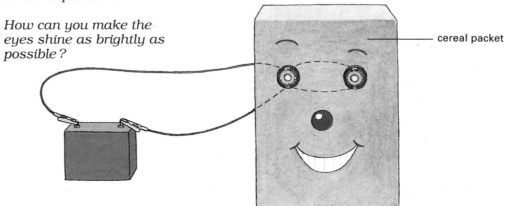

cereal packet

Here are some electrical games that you can make.

How steady is your hand?

track made from coat hanger wire

coat hanger wire

wooden block

buzzer

connect battery between here

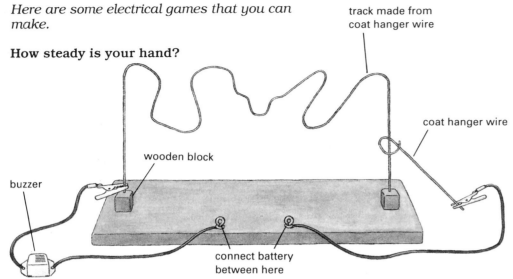

How far can you get along the track before you touch the wire and make the buzzer sound?

Make a mystery spider

Thread each of four wires through two holes. Tie knots to keep them in place. Put the top back up on the tub.

margarine tub

knots to keep wire in place

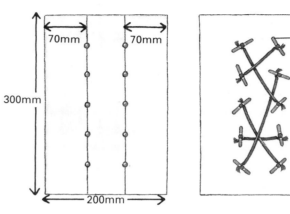

Using a simple circuit made up of a battery and bulb, can you find which 'legs' are connected?

Make a quiz board

Cut stiff card to size. Draw two vertical parallel lines. Make five pairs of holes as shown.

70mm   70mm

300mm

200mm

brass paper fastener

Push a brass paper fastener through each hole and open it out at the back of the card. Connect pairs of fasteners from each side together with wire. Make sure the ends of the wires are stripped bare so that there is a good connection with the fasteners. Arrange questions and answers to fit connected pairs of paper fasteners.

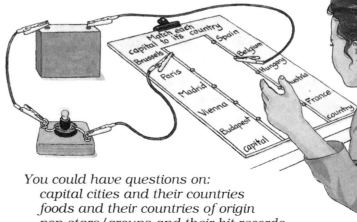

You could have questions on:
capital cities and their countries
foods and their countries of origin
pop-stars/groups and their hit records

Check your answers with a simple circuit.

Make a water timer

Cut the top off a washing-up liquid container.

Cut a round piece of polystyrene with a slightly smaller diameter than the washing-up liquid container. Cover it with aluminium foil. This will form a float.

Make a hole in the base of another washing-up liquid container. Cover the hole in the bottom with masking tape. Fill the bottle with water.

Set up the circuit shown to an electric bell or buzzer.

Hold the water bottle upside down above the cut-down washing-up liquid container. When the masking tape is removed from the bottom of the bottle, water runs into the container and causes the float to rise. When it touches the bare wires the circuit is completed and the bell rings.

washing-up liquid container

polystyrene

polystyrene float covered with kitchen foil

hole

remove masking tape to allow the water to run out

second washing-up liquid container

How can you adjust the time it takes between removing the tape from the water bottle and the bell ringing? Make up games which require 1 minute, 2 minute and 3 minute timers.

Send messages to each other

Make up two blocks like these.

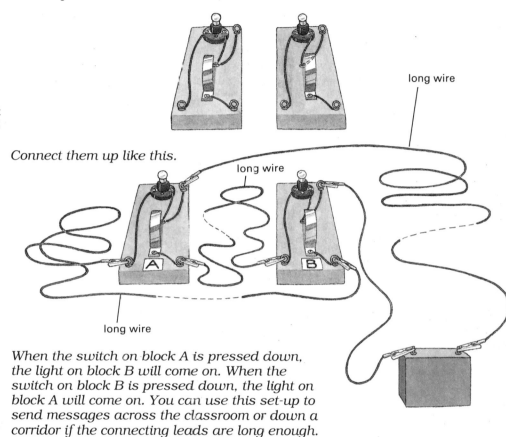

Connect them up like this.

long wire

long wire

A

long wire

B

When the switch on block A is pressed down, the light on block B will come on. When the switch on block B is pressed down, the light on block A will come on. You can use this set-up to send messages across the classroom or down a corridor if the connecting leads are long enough.

Try sending messages in Morse code.

letters			numbers
A . _	J . _ _ _	S . . .	0 _ _ _ _ _
B _ . . .	K _ . _	T _	1 . _ _ _ _
C _ . _ .	L . _ . .	U . . _	2 . . _ _ _
D _ . .	M _ _	V . . . _	3 . . . _ _
E .	N _ .	W . _ _	4 . . . . _
F . . _ .	O _ _ _	X _ . . _	5 . . . . .
G _ _ .	P . _ _ .	Y _ . _ _	6 _ . . . .
H	Q _ _ . _	Z _ _ . .	7 _ _ . . .
I . .	R . _ .		8 _ _ _ . .
			9 _ _ _ _ .

The length of a dash should be about twice that of a dot. Let the children experiment with this and also decide how to 'space' letters and words.

Circuits containing batteries, bulbs, switches and other electrical components can all be shown using symbols. This relieves the tedium of making a full drawing of every circuit every time you want to keep a record.

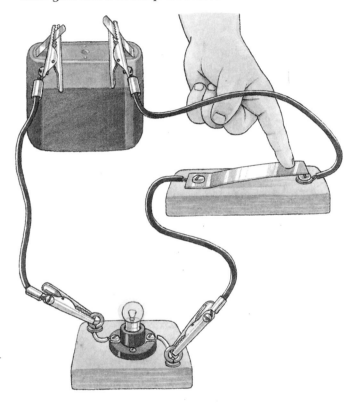

The circuit above becomes

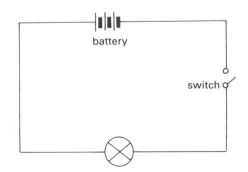

This is the circuit diagram for three bulbs connected in series.

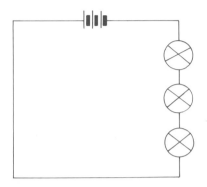

This is the circuit diagram for three bulbs in parallel.

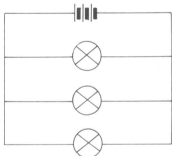

Some common symbols

single cell

battery (a number of cells connected in series)

switch

bulb

coil of wire

Printed circuits

Many circuits are made using tiny threads of wire. Such circuits are called printed circuits.

You can make a simple 'printed circuit'.

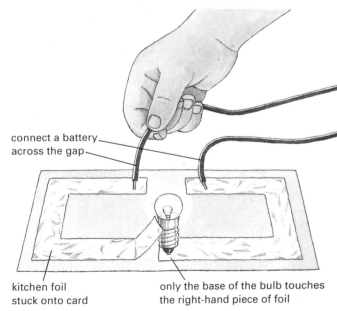

connect a battery across the gap

kitchen foil stuck onto card

only the base of the bulb touches the right-hand piece of foil

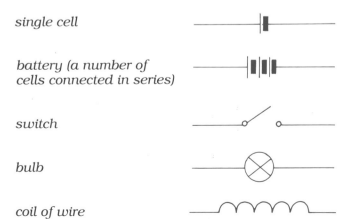

Wrap some insulated wire around a plotting (or charm) compass as shown below. It can be a little tricky to hold in place, but persevere!

plotting compass

Press the switch. Observe the deflection of the compass needle. Do it again to check that it is the position of the switch which is controlling the deflection.

When an electric current passes through a wire, a magnetic field is produced near the wire. The field is often very weak; however, it can be detected.

In this experiment, the magnetic field set up by the passing current interfered with the magnetic field of the compass needle. (The needle, of course, is a suspended tiny magnet.)

Make some current detectors

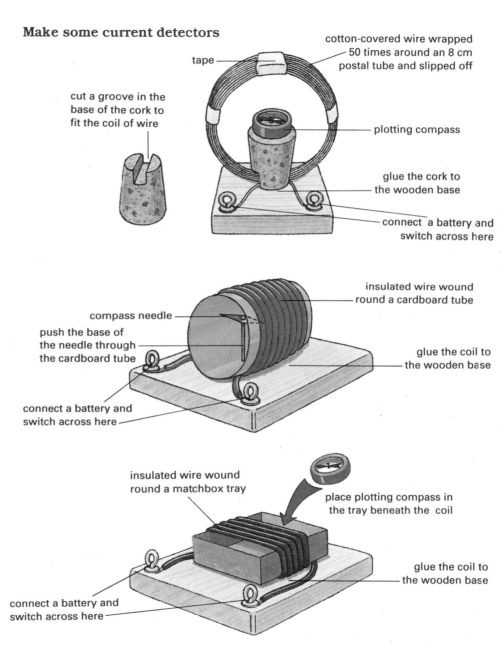

cotton-covered wire wrapped 50 times around an 8 cm postal tube and slipped off

tape

cut a groove in the base of the cork to fit the coil of wire

plotting compass

glue the cork to the wooden base

connect a battery and switch across here

insulated wire wound round a cardboard tube

compass needle

push the base of the needle through the cardboard tube

glue the coil to the wooden base

connect a battery and switch across here

insulated wire wound round a matchbox tray

place plotting compass in the tray beneath the coil

glue the coil to the wooden base

connect a battery and switch across here

Current detectors like these are called galvanometers. They are named after the Italian scientist Luigi Galvani.

You can make an electromagnet by wrapping insulated copper wire (0.31 mm or 30 swg) around a soft iron rod. Wrap several hundred turns of wire neatly around a rod. Secure the ends with masking tape.

Set up this circuit.

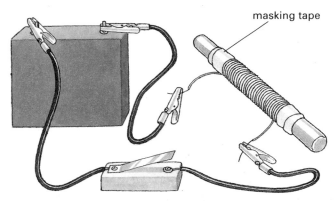

masking tape

The magnetic effect produced by passing a current through the coil can be demonstrated by dipping the bar into a saucer holding small nails or paper clips.

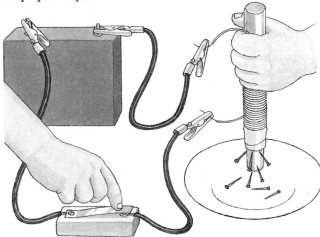

How many nails can you pick up?

Remember, electromagnets drain batteries very quickly.

Compare the strength of electromagnets

Make up some electromagnets, each with a known number of turns of wire.

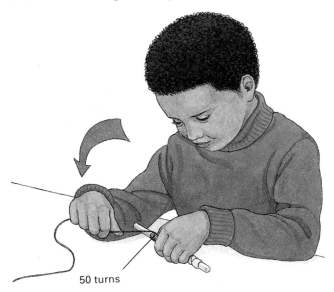

50 turns

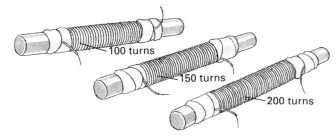

100 turns
150 turns
200 turns

Find out how many nails each can pick up. What effect does the number of turns have on the number of nails picked up?

To make the test fairer, you could start with an electromagnet with 200 turns. Test it. Unwrap 50 turns and test the 150-turn electromagnet. Then unwrap a further 50 turns to achieve a 100-turn electromagnet and so on. In this way, the same length of wire is used in the circuit each time and so the current flowing each time is similar.

Examine an electric bell

Remove the cover from an electric bell to show how an electromagnet is used in a 'make and break' circuit.

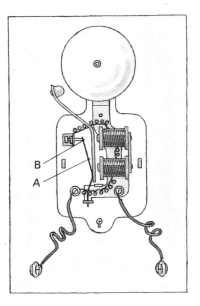

B
A

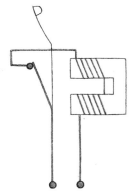

When the electricity is switched on, the electromagnets come on and attract the steel strip (A). As soon as this happens, the circuit is broken at B. The steel strip then springs back because the electromagnet goes off. And so the cycle repeats.

Howzat!

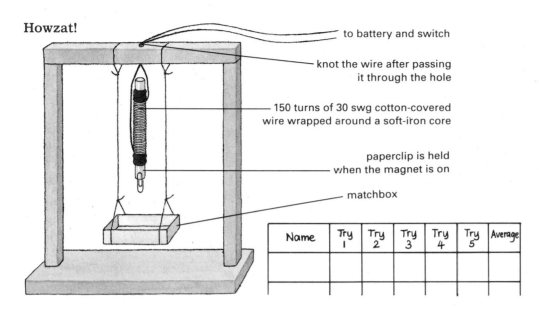

- to battery and switch
- knot the wire after passing it through the hole
- 150 turns of 30 swg cotton-covered wire wrapped around a soft-iron core
- paperclip is held when the magnet is on
- matchbox

Name	Try 1	Try 2	Try 3	Try 4	Try 5	Average

Set the matchbox swinging. Can you release the paperclip so that it is 'caught' by the swing?

Crane

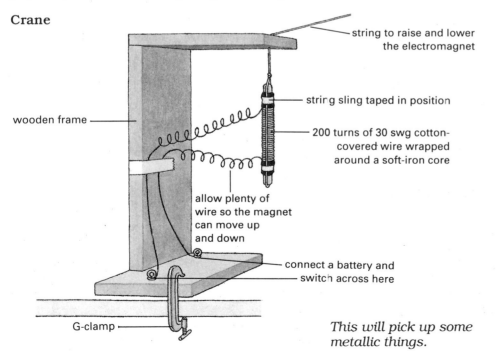

- string to raise and lower the electromagnet
- string sling taped in position
- 200 turns of 30 swg cotton-covered wire wrapped around a soft-iron core
- wooden frame
- allow plenty of wire so the magnet can move up and down
- connect a battery and switch across here
- G-clamp

This will pick up some metallic things.

Clacker

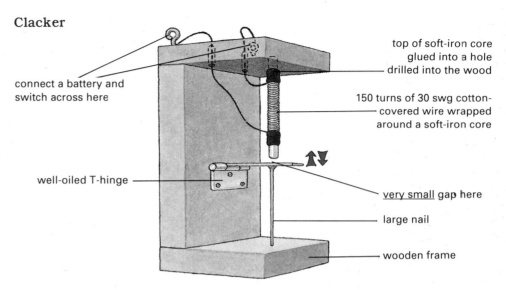

- connect a battery and switch across here
- top of soft-iron core glued into a hole drilled into the wood
- 150 turns of 30 swg cotton-covered wire wrapped around a soft-iron core
- well-oiled T-hinge
- <u>very small</u> gap here
- large nail
- wooden frame

When you switch the magnet on and off, the hinge moves up and down, so making a clacking noise. You could use this set-up to send messages.

Roundabout

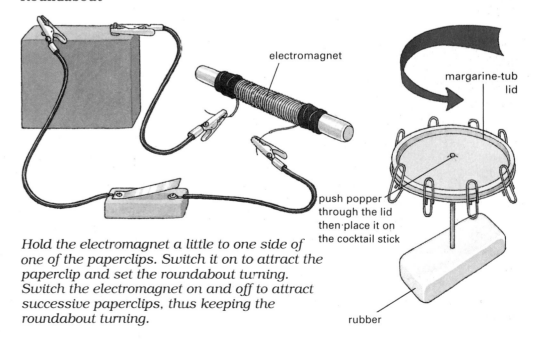

- electromagnet
- margarine-tub lid
- push popper through the lid then place it on the cocktail stick
- rubber

Hold the electromagnet a little to one side of one of the paperclips. Switch it on to attract the paperclip and set the roundabout turning. Switch the electromagnet on and off to attract successive paperclips, thus keeping the roundabout turning.

It is very easy to generate electricity chemically. The amounts made are very small so you need a sensitive instrument to detect them – a galvanometer.

Make a strong mixture of salt and water.

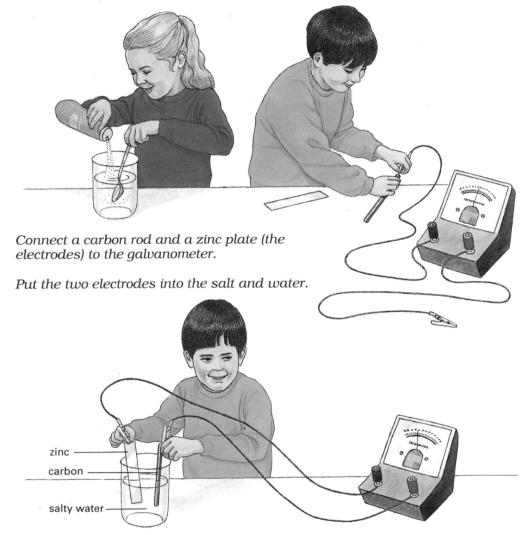

Connect a carbon rod and a zinc plate (the electrodes) to the galvanometer.

Put the two electrodes into the salt and water.

zinc
carbon
salty water

The galvanometer registers the flow of current. Try swopping over the electrodes. What happens to the needle?

Try it with vinegar.

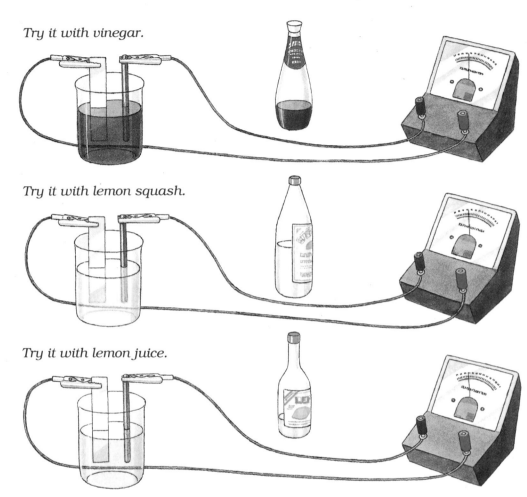

Try it with lemon squash.

Try it with lemon juice.

Try it with baking powder (in solution).

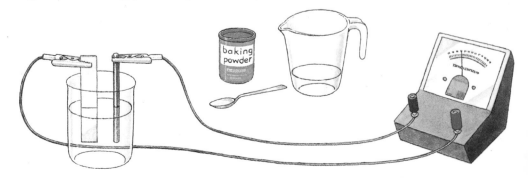

Try different electrodes.

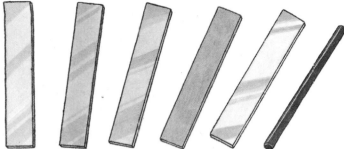

zinc copper brass lead tin carbon

Experiment with the size of electrodes. Try different pairings in salty water.

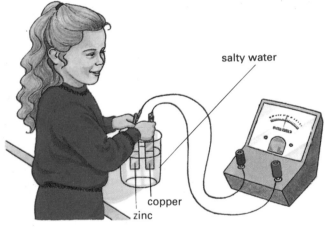

salty water

copper
zinc

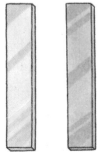 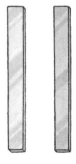

zinc copper   zinc copper

Try making electricity with a lemon

Free the juice from the lemon by rolling it hard with the palm of your hand on a table.

Stick the electrodes into it. Watch what happens to the galvanometer needle.

zinc copper

Simple cells

In a simple cell the two metals react with an acid. There is a difference in the energies of the electrons in the two electrodes. This is an electrical potential-energy difference – what we commonly call voltage. Electrons flow from one plate to the other and a current passes around the circuit. (Hydrogen bubbles off at the negative electrode and oxygen at the positive electrode.)

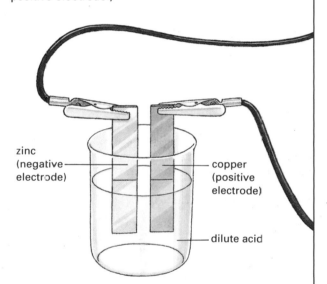

zinc
(negative
electrode)

copper
(positive
electrode)

dilute acid

There are problems with such a cell:
- The electrodes are always reacting even when the cell is not connected in a circuit, for example to a bulb. They are, therefore, slowly eaten away.
- Hydrogen bubbles pass to the copper plate and gather on its surface. This is called polarisation. It slows the reaction, and if a bulb is connected in the circuit it will be seen to gradually dim. (See page 7 for the structure of a dry cell where manganese dioxide is used to prevent this build up of hydrogen ions.)

You can show the discovery that the English scientist Michael Faraday made in Victorian England.

Wind a large coil of cotton covered copper wire (30 swg). Connect the coil to a galvanometer.

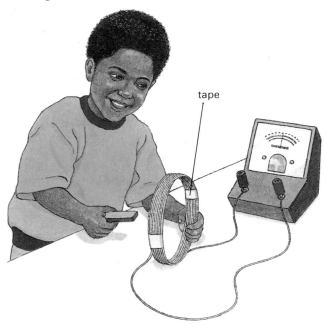

tape

Thrust a strong bar magnet in and out of the coil. Watch the galvanometer. The movement of the magnet in the coil generates electricity.

This is the basic principle used to generate electricity in a power station or from a bicycle dynamo. Both rely on a coil of wire and a magnet.

Bicycle dynamo

Take a bicycle dynamo to pieces. Show the children the rotating magnet and the coil of wire.

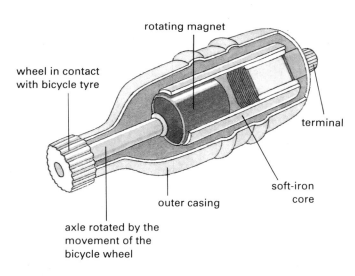

rotating magnet

wheel in contact with bicycle tyre

terminal

soft-iron core

outer casing

axle rotated by the movement of the bicycle wheel

If you connect the ends of the coil to a 1.5V or 2.5V bulb, and turn the magnet by hand, you will get a flash of light from the bulb.

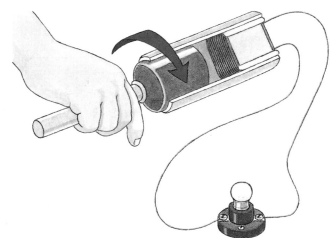

Try riding a bicycle with the dynamo light on, and then with the dynamo off. Which is easier? You cannot get energy for nothing!

Power stations

In a power station, the magnet and the coil of wire are both in what is called the generator.

When oil, coal, or gas is burnt, the energy released is used to boil water to make steam. The steam is used to produce kinetic energy, by using the force of it to turn large windmill-like devices called turbines. These are connected to the generator and cause the coil to spin, thus generating electricity.

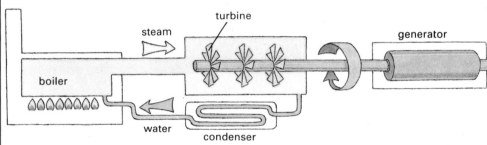

The electricity generated goes to a transformer, where it is converted to a very high voltage (400 kilowatts) before joining the National Grid. 'An Early Start to the Environment' (page 92) explains how electricity is distributed.

Energy chains

The energy chain of a power station is an interesting one. Fuel burns and the resulting heat is used to boil water and produce steam. The steam is compressed and passes through turbines causing them to rotate. As they rotate they turn the generator. Thus the energy chain is:

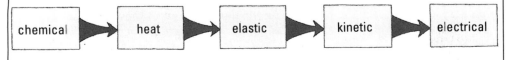

chemical → heat → elastic → kinetic → electrical

Model power station

You can buy a model power station from scientific suppliers. It consists of a small steam engine, a dynamo and a bank of bulbs.

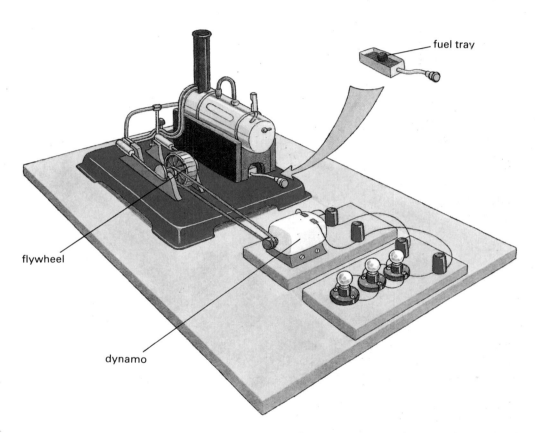

Put the lighted fuel tray under the engine's boiler. When the water is boiling, open the steam valve. Gently nudge the flywheel to get it going. The belt drive then turns the dynamo. The electricity generated is used to light the bulbs.

What happens to the speed of the engine if you alter the number of bulbs in the circuit? Try it with one, two and three bulbs.

Make an electric motor

When one magnetic effect is influenced by another, a force is produced. This effect is used in electric motors. It is possible for older juniors to make one from scratch, but it is advisable to buy an electric motor in kit form to ensure a working model.

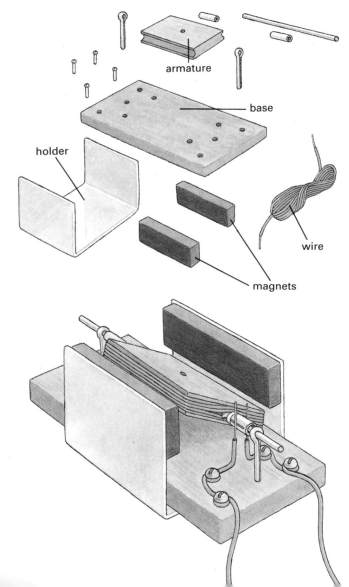

armature

base

holder

wire

magnets

Here is a home-made motor, but it can be fiddly to get going.

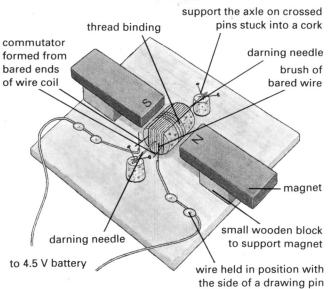

commutator formed from bared ends of wire coil

thread binding

support the axle on crossed pins stuck into a cork

darning needle

brush of bared wire

magnet

darning needle

small wooden block to support magnet

to 4.5 V battery

wire held in position with the side of a drawing pin

It is crucial that the two brushes just make contact with bare wires from the cork, which is wrapped with 30 turns of wire (the armature). Spin the armature by hand to set it going.

How does an electric motor work?

A coil carrying an electric current behaves like a flat bar magnet, with one side acting as a north pole and the other as a south pole. In the diagram, the top side of the coil is shown as a south pole.

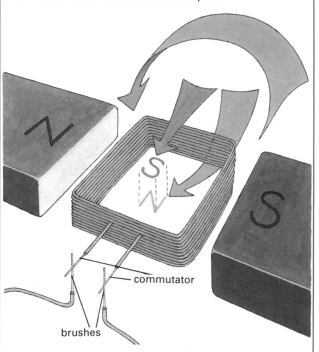

commutator

brushes

Because of the attraction of the 'south pole' of the coil to the north pole of the permanent magnet, the coil rotates anticlockwise. The lower side of the coil is, of course, a north pole and is attracted by the south pole of the permanent magnet.

The rotation of the coil results in the bare wires of the commutator touching the opposite brushes. This reverses the current in the coil and what was the south face of the coil, becomes the north which is repelled by the north pole of the magnet. In this way the coil continues to rotate.

Look at different uses of electric motors with the children. See 'An Early Start to Technology' (pages 33 and 41) for further details on motor-driven vehicles.

Make some motor-driven vehicles

belt-driven trolley

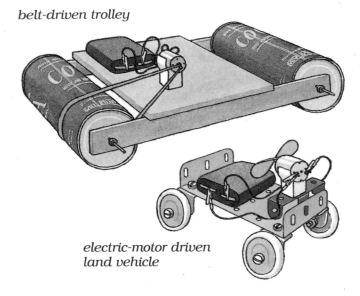

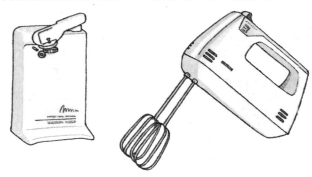

electric-motor driven land vehicle

'An Early Start to Technology' (pages 33 and 41) gives full construction details.

How are motors used?

Look at how motors are used in the kitchen.

Look for other uses of motors in the home.

Look at the different uses electric motors are put to outdoors.

Look in the workshop for things driven by motors.

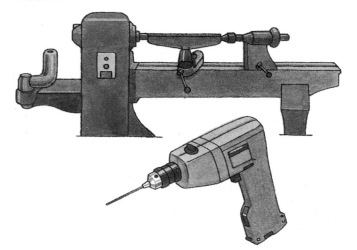

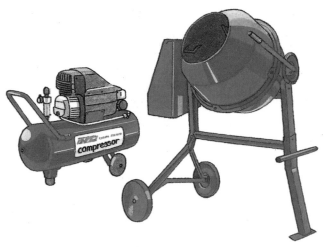

Short circuits and fuses

Most children are familiar with the need to replace the fuse in a plug from time to time. To understand the function of a fuse children have first to understand the nature of a short circuit.

What is a short circuit?

Set up a simple circuit using <u>bare</u> wire. Make sure the bulb lights.

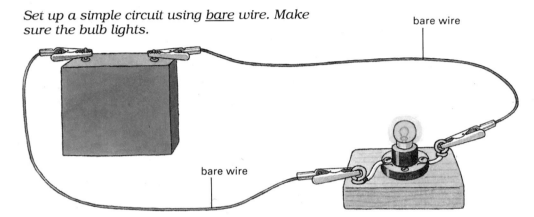

bare wire

bare wire

Connect a wire across the circuit like this. The bulb goes out.

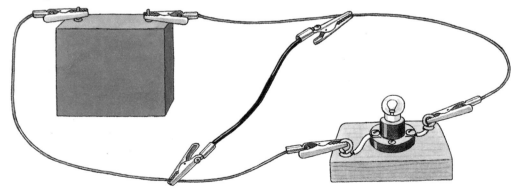

Instead of passing through the bulb and having to do work to produce heat and light, the current takes the easier pathway through the wire – a short circuit. You will find that the wires can get quite hot.

Short circuits like this are wasteful as they drain batteries quickly. With mains electricity, a similar situation is very dangerous. It can result in a fire, as sometimes happens when wires get worn and frayed and cause a short circuit.

steel wool

To reduce the dangers of such short circuits, a safety device called a fuse is built into a circuit.

Set up a circuit like this. Press the switch and check that the bulb lights.

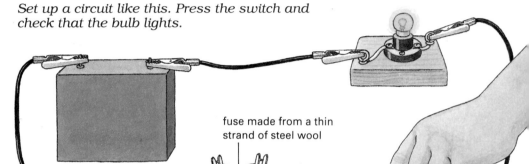

fuse made from a thin strand of steel wool

Short-circuit the bulb as shown by using a short piece of wire connected to crocodile clips. Watch the steel wool (the fuse) when you press the switch. The current surges directly through it and it burns out.

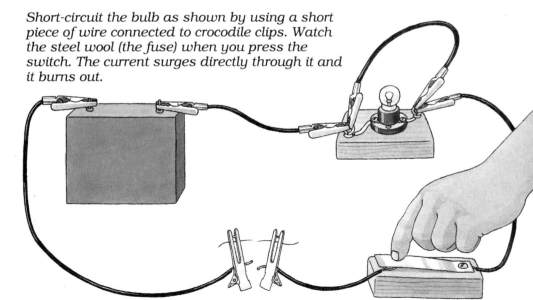

Fuses

Electricity cables enter the home near the electricity meter and fuse box.

Modern wiring uses a ring circuit for sockets. The cables carry electricity to the sockets where appliances can be plugged in. The circuit passes through the fuse box.

—— live
—— neutral
—— earth

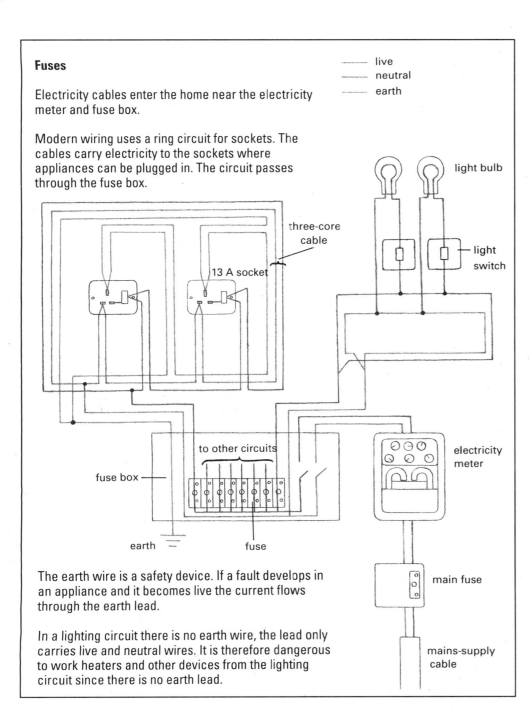

light bulb

light switch

three-core cable

13 A socket

to other circuits

fuse box

earth

fuse

electricity meter

main fuse

mains-supply cable

The earth wire is a safety device. If a fault develops in an appliance and it becomes live the current flows through the earth lead.

In a lighting circuit there is no earth wire, the lead only carries live and neutral wires. It is therefore dangerous to work heaters and other devices from the lighting circuit since there is no earth lead.

Look at the fuse box in school.

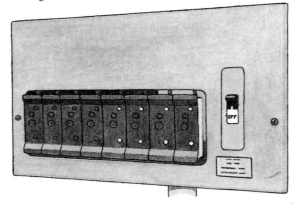

live lead
earth pin
live pin
earth lead
neutral pin
neutral lead
fuse

Many appliances are connected to a plug which carries its own fuse.

It is important to emphasise to the children the dangers of mains electricity and to remind them that they should never open up plugs, unless supervised by an adult, or poke things into a socket.

inside a fuse

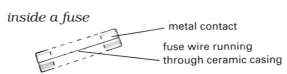

metal contact
fuse wire running through ceramic casing

Fuses have different amperage values.

The fuse wire in a power circuit to a cooker is 30 amps. In a lighting circuit it is 5 amps.

It is easy to work out what amperage fuse to use in a plug.

$$current = \frac{power\ rating\ of\ appliance}{mains\ voltage}$$

So for a 600 watt food mixer, using a mains voltage of 240 volts,

$$current = \frac{600}{240} = 2.5\ amp$$

Therefore, the correct fuse to use is a 3 amp one.

Look at some of the electrical objects around the home and the school. Make careful drawings of some of them.

FUSED

Get the children to make a cut-away drawing of their own home, showing all the electrical things. Mark the position of the power sockets. Make lists of the different types of equipment.

Kitchen

hand mixer
washing machine
clothes drier
iron
fridge – freezer
food processor
coffee percolator
kettle
cooker
power points
ceiling light

Airing cupboard

immersion heater
central heating pump

Bedrooms

hairdryer
power point
ceiling light
train set
computer
lamps

Bathroom

shower
toothbrush
ceiling lamp
wall light
shaver point

Lounge

lamps
TV and video
vacuum cleaner
hi-fi
wall lamps
power points
ceiling light

Workshop

lawn mower
car track
drill
battery charger
power points
wall light

Garden

wall light
fountain pump
electricity meter

The phenomenon of attracting materials by rubbing rods of amber has been know since ancient times. The word 'electricity' is derived from the Greek word for amber: 'elektron'.

Much later, Dr William Gilbert, who was physician to Queen Elizabeth I, pursued experiments with electricity, and Benjamin Franklin experimented with kites and lightning. The latter's experiments in 1752, dangerous as they were, established that lightning was caused by electricity, and led to practical application of this knowledge in the lightning conductor.

William Gilbert demonstrating electrical experiments to Queen Elizabeth I.

Benjamin Franklin flying a kite in a thunderstorm.

Luigi Galvani dissecting frogs' legs.

In 1780 Luigi Galvani, Professor of Anatomy at Bologna University, made an important discovery while dissecting a frog. He found that a frog's leg twitched if touched by two dissimilar metals such as copper and zinc.

It is said that he made the discovery by accident when he hung a frog by a brass pin and its leg accidentally touched an iron railing below. There is also the, probably apocryphal, tale of Mrs Galvani, who is said to have noticed the phenomenon when cooking frogs' legs in an iron pan and using a metal spoon to stir them!

Galvani realised that the twitching of the leg was due to electricity. He, incorrectly, attributed the source of the electricity to the frog. The phenomenon become known as galvanism.

Alessandro Volta (1745-1827) was Professor of Natural Philosophy at Pavia University in Northern Italy. He became interested in Galvani's discovery. He was not convinced that the source of electricity lay in the frog. He looked for an explanation that was compatible with the fact that electricity could be produced by rubbing.

Volta suggested that the electricity came from a reaction between the iron and brass metals that Galvani used, and that the twitching of the frog's leg merely served as an indication of the flow of electricity.

In 1800, just a year after Galvani's death, Volta produced what is now called a Voltaic pile – the world's first battery. Volta used discs of zinc and copper piled on one another in salt water.

The discovery was of tremendous importance because it provided the basis for a continuous and cheap source of electricity.

When Volta tried to give up his professorship in 1804, Napoleon, who governed Europe at that time, said, 'I cannot agree to Volta's resignation. He may even give only one lecture a year, but the University of Pavia would be wounded to the heart if I were to allow so famous a name to be struck off the roll of its members; furthermore a good general must die upon the field of honour.'

Page 70 shows a method of constructing a simple cell which uses the same principle as Volta's pile.

The drawback with Volta's pile was that the bubbles of hydrogen released in the reaction gathered on the copper, and eventually stopped the chemical reaction taking place.

Leclanché found a way to stop this. He used carbon instead of copper, and, most importantly, surrounded the carbon with a substance rich in oxygen: manganese dioxide. The oxygen combined with the hydrogen to form water. The troublesome film of hydrogen bubbles was thus removed. This was the forerunner of today's dry cell.

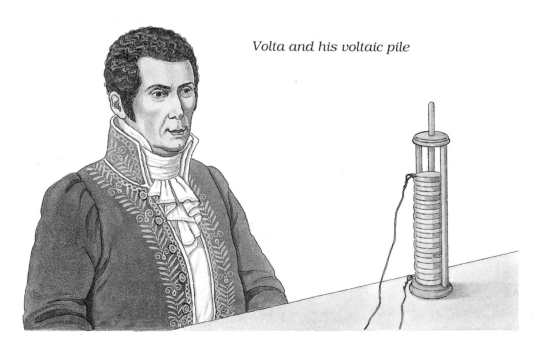

Volta and his voltaic pile

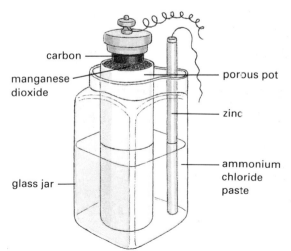

carbon

manganese dioxide

porous pot

zinc

glass jar

ammonium chloride paste

Leclanché cell and its modern-day equivalent

The link between electricity and magnetism was first demonstrated in 1819 by Hans Christian Oersted, Professor of Physics at the University of Copenhagen. He discovered it quite by chance.

When lecturing to his students he happened to have a compass lying on the demonstration table near to an electric circuit that he was using. When he switched on the circuit, he noticed that the compass needle (which is a tiny magnet) turned at right angles to the wire. He repeated the effect several times.

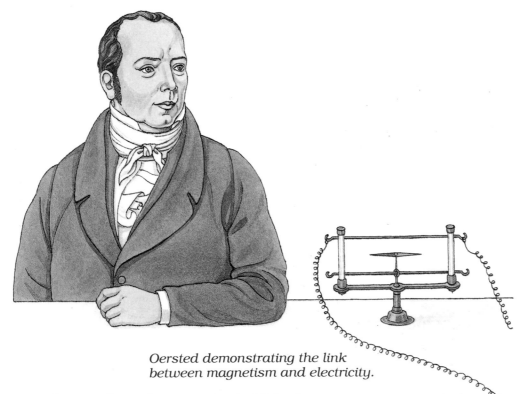

Oersted demonstrating the link between magnetism and electricity.

One of Oersted's students, writing to Michael Faraday, the famous English scientist, said that Oersted was 'quite struck with perplexity for he had not any more idea than any other person that the force would be transversal (at right angles).'

The discovery that electricity can be produced by using a magnet is due to Michael Faraday (1791-1867).

Michael Faraday was the son of a blacksmith. He received only an elementary education and left school at thirteen to work for a bookseller. A course of lectures given by the chemist Sir Humphry Davy at the Royal Institution, when Faraday was twenty, so fired his enthusiasm that he sought a job with Davy.

He was appointed as a laboratory assistant at the Royal Institution and rose to become its superintendent. He married and lived above the Royal Institution laboratory in Albemarle Street for 46 years.

For many years he wrestled with the problem of producing electricity using magnetism. Indeed, it is said that he carried a magnet and coil of wire about with him to remind himself of the problem.

In 1831, Faraday induced a current in a coil by plunging in a bar magnet. He went on to produce a machine that generated a continuous current – the first dynamo. Page 72 explains how you can achieve both these affects.

Michael Faraday

It is well known that the smallest particle of a material that can exist by itself is called a molecule. H_2O is the symbol used to represent a molecule of water. Molecules are made up of atoms. A water molecule contains two hydrogen atoms and one oxygen atom.

Atoms themselves are made of even smaller particles. Its central core is composed of protons and neutrons. Moving outside this core are electrons. It is the <u>movement</u> of electrons that we call an electric current.

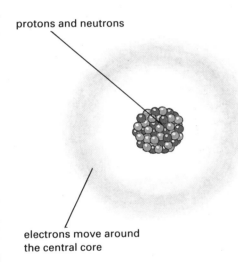

protons and neutrons

electrons move around the central core

In metals, the electrons are loosely held to their atoms. It is this which makes metals good conductors of electricity.

An analogy to explain electricity

The following analogy of electricity to a flow of water has its drawbacks, but it may help to explain some electrical phenomena in fairly straightforward terms.

In any flow of current there are three factors to be considered:

Intensity factor

This is electrical potential. It is measured in volts. It is the pressure difference between electrons flowing from a region of higher electron concentration to a lower one.

Water flows from a region of higher pressure to one of a lower pressure; for example a stream flowing down a mountain or water flowing from a dam.

Just as it would be possible to measure the pressure of the water in the dam without allowing any flow of water, so it is possible to measure the pressure of electrons. It is this pressure that we measure as electrical potential or voltage.

Quantity factor

This is the current or amount of flow. It is measured in amperes.

You can turn on a water tap and allow the water to flow strongly or gently. The same can be done with an electric current: you can let a lot of current through or a little.

Resistance factor

The resistance is offered by the conductor. It is measured in ohms.

If water is flowing through pipes, it stands to reason that a pipe of narrow diameter is going to conduct water more slowly than one of wide diameter. In a sense, we can say the pipe of narrow diameter offers more resistance than one of wide diameter to carrying water.

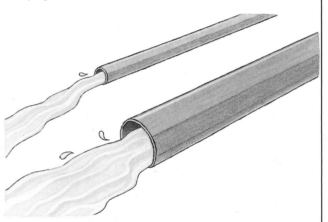

Similarly, a thin copper wire offers more resistance to a flow of current than a thick copper wire. The pressure or potential may be the same in each case, but the flow of current is different.

Ohm's Law

There is a famous law showing the relationship between these three factors. It is called Ohm's Law.

$$E = IR$$

Where
  E is the potential (measured in volts)
  I is the current (measured in amperes)
  R is the resistance (measured in ohms).

The earliest observed electrical effects did not involve batteries or dynamos, but were the result of static electricity.

Combing your hair or taking off a nylon garment often causes crackling. You may get a small shock if you cross a nylon carpet and then touch a metal filing cabinet.

We say things have become charged with static electricity'. These electric charges are not made by rubbing your hair, clothes or feet, they are already there.

All materials are made of atoms. Within the atom there are electrically charged particles. Normally an object has a balance between the positive and negative charges in it - we say it is neutral. However, the two kinds of charge can be separated by rubbing. Objects are then said to be charged.

When you do experiments on static electricity, it is best to have all materials as dry as possible. Keep them over a warm radiator for a while before you use them. If possible, wait for a dry day.

Bending water

Rub a plastic comb on your sleeve. Hold it near a trickle of water from a tap.

The water is attracted towards the comb.

Jumping paper

Run a plastic comb through your hair. Hold it near some small pieces of torn paper.

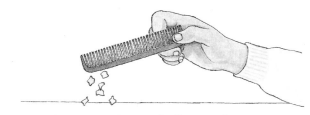

The paper jumps up towards the comb.

Attractive hair

Rub a comb on your sleeve. Hold it near to someone's hair.

It attracts a few hairs towards it.

Sticky balloons

Rub a balloon on a pullover. Stick it to the wall.

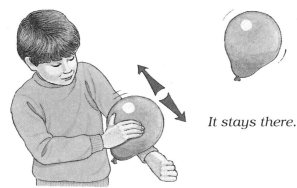

It stays there.

Dancing figures

Cut out some paper dancers.

Take a sheet of brown wrapping paper, which has been warmed on top of a radiator. Brush it quickly with wool so that it becomes highly charged. Hold it over the paper dancers.

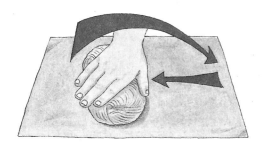

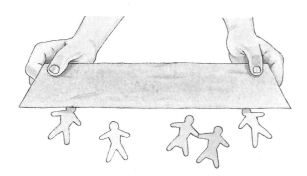

The paper figures will 'dance' on the table top.

Investigate how charged objects react with each other.

How do charged objects react with each other?

Rub a polythene rod against some wool. The friction of the rubbing causes negative charges (electrons) to flow from the wool to the polythene, so the rod becomes negatively charged and the silk positively charged.

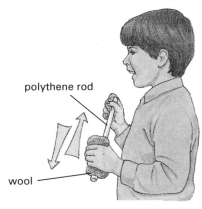

polythene rod

wool

Rub some acetate (or glass) against silk. Electrons pass from the acetate to the silk. The silk becomes negatively charged and the acetate becomes positively charged.

silk

glass

You now have a negatively charged polythene rod and a positively charged piece of acetate.

Hang a balloon from the edge of a table.

Rub the balloon with wool. It will become negatively charged.

Test your charged polythene rod and piece of acetate by bringing each, in turn, to a <u>freshly</u> charged balloon.

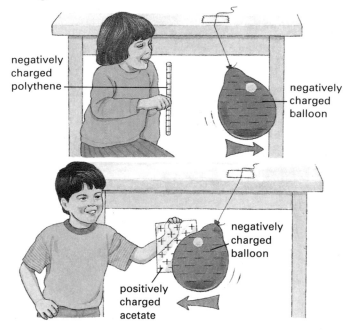

negatively charged polythene

negatively charged balloon

negatively charged balloon

positively charged acetate

You will find that:
  like charges repel each other
  unlike charges attract each other.

Rub two balloons with wool and bring them near one another. What happens?

Cut two strips of polythene from a plastic bag.

Hold the two strips together from one hand. Charge them by stroking each one between the finger and thumb of the other hand. What happens?

Lightning

A flash of lightning is one of the most spectacular effects of static electricity in the natural world.

It has been known for thousands of years that magnetite (Fe_3O_4), a naturally occurring rock, possesses the power to attract iron. It was so named because it was originally found in Magnesia, Asia Minor.

In the 'Tale of the Porter and the Young Girls' from the 'Book of One Thousand and One Nights', there is the 'Tale of the Third Kalandar'. The story tells of a black mountain which is covered with the nails of ships because of its terrible magnetic power.

As the story says, 'Hardly had morning come when we reached the mountain of magnetic rocks; the waves drove us alongside, and all the thousands of nails on our ten ships were suddenly wrenched away and flew to join themselves to the mountain. The ships opened out and fell asunder and we were thrown into the sea.'

When magnetite is suspended freely it ends up pointing in a north/south direction. This was known to the Chinese as long ago as 2500 BC. They used to make silken cradles in which to hang a piece of magnetite, thus forming a primitive compass. Magnetite became known as lodestone (leading stone).

William Gilbert, court physician to Queen Elizabeth I, was greatly interested in magnetism. He produced the first important scientific book on the subject to appear in England. It was written in Latin and was published in 1600. It was called 'On the Magnet and Magnetic Bodies and on the Great Magnet the Earth'.

Buy a collection of magnets. You will need a variety of magnets so you can do a range of experiments.

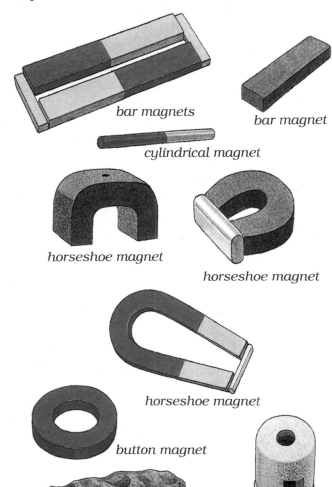

bar magnets

bar magnet

cylindrical magnet

horseshoe magnet

horseshoe magnet

horseshoe magnet

button magnet

pot magnet

lodestone

It is best to buy well-made magnets, even though they are initially expensive, as they last much longer. The ones made from alloys such as Alnico (aluminium-nickel-cobalt) are good.

Domain theory of magnetism

Iron, nickel and cobalt have magnetic properties; other metals do not. One theory of magnetism suggests that groups of molecules form domains. Each domain acts like a small magnet. In a non-magnetised substance the domains are mixed up.

domains

If the domains are lined up, their magnetic effects reinforce each other to make a magnet.

The domains can be lined up in a magnetic material simply by putting the material against a magnet.

Make a temporary magnet

A permanent magnet will pick up a paperclip. A large unmagnetised nail will not, unless it is touching a magnet – in which case, it will pick up the paperclip.

This effect is only <u>temporary</u>. *If the magnet is removed from the nail, the paperclip will fall. This is because the domains in the nail spring back to their normal jumbled up positions and the magnetism is lost.*

Make a permanent magnet

To make a <u>permanent</u> *magnet, stroke a thin iron bar with a magnet. Only stroke in one direction. The magnet pulls the domains in the iron rod into line.*

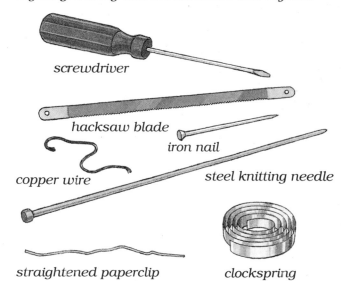

Try magnetising various materials and objects.

screwdriver

hacksaw blade

copper wire

iron nail

steel knitting needle

straightened paperclip

clockspring

What materials are attracted to a magnet?

Collect lots of things. Test them to see if they are attracted to a magnet.

Test the magnet against fixtures in the room. Keep a record of what happens.

Attracted by a magnet	Not attracted by a magnet
scissors	pencil
fire extinguisher	marble

All the things attracted by a magnet contain iron. Objects made of cobalt or nickel would be attracted too, but these are uncommon. (Make sure you keep magnets away from any delicate equipment which might be affected by them.)

Magnetic sorting

Make some mixtures to sort with a magnet.

iron and brass screws   pins mixed in sawdust

How strong is a magnet?

How many small nails can children hang end to end from one place on a magnet? Try this from various places on the magnet.

The magnetism is strongest at the ends or <u>poles</u> of the magnet, for these hold most nails.

Try different types of bar magnets.

Compare the strength of other types of magnets.

Can you sort your magnets in order of strength by this test?

Here are other ways to test the strength of magnets.

Unbend a paperclip to make a hook. Use a magnet placed on a ruler suspended between books to hold the hook. Hang paperclips from the hook. How many will it hold?

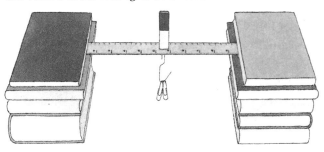

Try each magnet in turn. Which is the strongest?

Suspend a small nail from a ruler as shown. Bring a magnet slowly towards the pin. From what distance is the pin attracted?

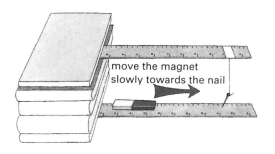

move the magnet slowly towards the nail

Keep a record of your results.

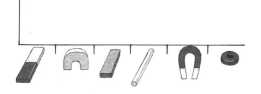

attraction

distance

Acting through things

Place a small nail on top of a ruler. Move a magnet slowly along under the ruler. Does it move the nail?

Can you move a nail inside a jam jar using a magnet outside the jar?

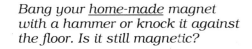

Can you use a magnet to pick up a small nail from the bottom of a bowl full of water without putting the magnet inside the water?

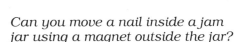

Magnets act through wood, glass and water. Find out what other things they will act through.

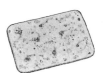

cork mat

ceramic tile

paper

 nylon shirt

 carpet tile

Keep records.

Magnets act through
wood
cork

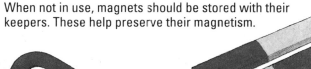

tin tray

 *leather shoe (try the thin leather at the sides)*

plastic bag

Demagnetising objects

Make a magnet.

Check your magnet works by seeing if it will attract paperclips.

Bang your <u>home-made</u> magnet with a hammer or knock it against the floor. Is it still magnetic?

Banging the magnet shakes up the domains and destroys the magnetism.

Another way to destroy the magnetism is to heat your <u>home-made</u> magnet in a flame.

tongs

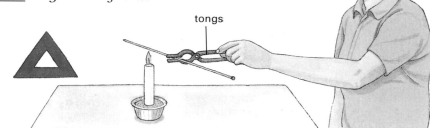

Banging magnets reduces their magnetism. They should always be handled carefully.

When not in use, magnets should be stored with their keepers. These help preserve their magnetism.

 keepers

Making words

Cut out about seventy squares of heavy paper, each about 5 cm x 5 cm. Write one letter from the alphabet on each. Make two complete alphabets and add in some extra vowels.

Attach a paperclip to each square of paper. Put all of them in a washing up bowl and mix them up.

cover the clip with tape so it doesn't catch on the other squares

Fish for letters with a magnet attached to a rod and line. Pass the rod around, taking one letter each time.

Who can make the most words in a given time?

Make a racing track

Cover the outer casing of a matchbox with recording tape from an old cassette. Secure it in place. This is your 'racing car'.

Draw a racing track on a sheet of strong card. You could use the side of a cardboard box. Support it between two tables.

Tape a magnet to the end of a metre rule and use it beneath the race track to move your car along.

magnet

metre rule

matchbox covered with recording tape

How good are you at keeping your car on the track? Who can get round the track the quickest?

Keep records.

Name	Time to get around course
Hameed	
Emma	

A variation is to stick cotton reels onto your card and make it into a slalom course. Who can complete the course the quickest?

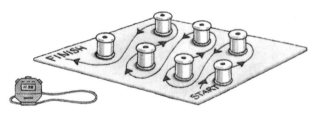

Do you get quicker with practice?

Indian rope trick

Tape a magnet to the end of a ruler. Set it so that it can attract a paperclip as shown.

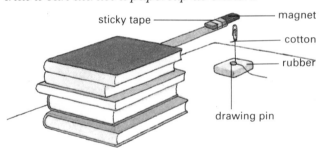

sticky tape — magnet

cotton

rubber

drawing pin

You will need to adjust the length of the cotton until you find the point where the magnet is strong enough to hold the paperclip without touching it.

Try putting various things in the space between the magnet and the paperclip. You could use one of the sets of metal discs available from scientific suppliers. The results are always illuminating for children.

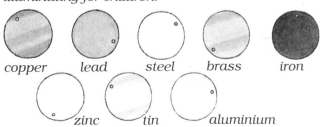

copper   lead   steel   brass   iron

zinc   tin   aluminium

Floating magnets

Stack button magnets on a thin piece of dowel or a garden cane.

Let children experiment to find out how they can get the button magnets to 'float' one above the other.

Find out how to position two bar magnets so that one 'floats' above the other. You will need to make a cradle for the magnets.

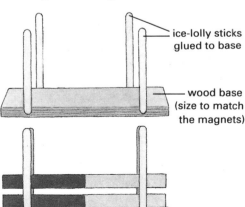

ice-lolly sticks glued to base

wood base (size to match the magnets)

Magnetic faces

Draw a face on thin card. Decorate it. Make a thin moustache from an old piece of recording tape. Use a magnet under the card to put the moustache in place.

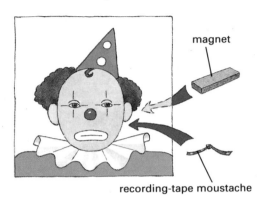

magnet

recording-tape moustache

Magnetic patterns

Put some vegetable oil into a jam jar. Stir in some iron filings.

Wrap a bar magnet in a plastic bag. Tie a piece of string to the bag so that you can lower the magnet into the jar of oil.

Can you see a three-dimensional pattern?

Magnetic boats

Make a paper boat from a piece of greaseproof paper about 200 mm square.

1 Fold the sides to the middle.

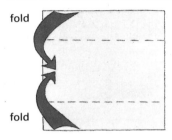

fold

fold

2 Fold the corners in along the dotted lines.

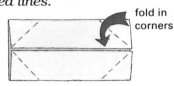

fold in corners

3 Crease and fold in as shown.

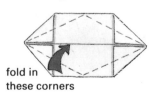

fold in these corners

then fold here

4 Open out and turn inside out.

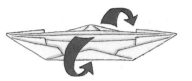

Attach a paperclip to the prow and put two washers in the base of the boat.

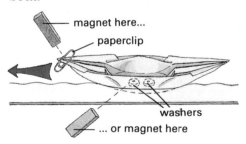

magnet here...

paperclip

washers

... or magnet here

You can move the boat along either by holding a magnet above the water and attracting the paperclip, or by holding the magnet beneath the water, so that it acts on the washers.

The north pole of a magnet is often marked with either a dot or an 'N'.

Let children play with matched pairs of magnets. Bring them together in the following ways.

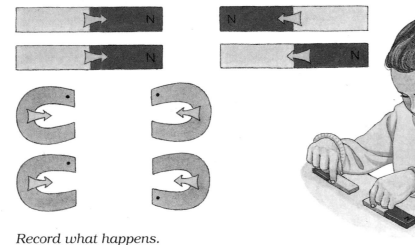

Record what happens.

The children will find that the two ends marked with a dot, or N, (the so-called north-seeking poles) repel one another, whereas a north-seeking pole will attract the opposite end (south-seeking pole) of the other magnet.

That is:
    like poles repel
    unlike poles attract.

The forces involved in attraction and repulsion can be demonstrated by placing a magnet in a paper sling and suspending it inside a cardboard box with two facing sides removed.

paper sling

Record the results when you bring another magnet towards the suspended magnet.

Magnet arrangement	Effect
North pole to North pole	
South pole to South pole	
South pole to North pole	
North pole to South pole	

A freely suspended magnet comes to rest in a north-south direction. It settles like this because it is affected by the Earth's magnetic field. It is the movement of liquid metals inside the Earth which cause the Earth to behave like a giant magnet.

A freely spinning magnet comes to rest in a north-south direction. This fact forms the basis of a compass.

Make a floating compass

Magnetise a steel sewing needle by stroking it with a magnet.

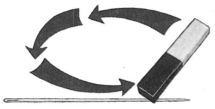

Push the needle through the top of a cork.

Stick a pin in the underside to act as a keel.

Float the cork in a bowl of water. A drop of washing-up liquid will reduce the surface tension and stop the cork moving to the side .

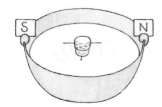

The cork will come to rest with the needle aligned north-south.

Make a free-standing compass

Use a magnetised steel knitting needle, pivoted as shown below.

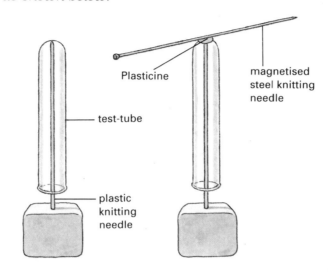

Plasticine

magnetised steel knitting needle

test-tube

plastic knitting needle

Magnetic north and North Pole

The Earth rotates on an axis with the North Pole at one end and the South Pole at the other. However, a compass points at the pole of the Earth's magnetic field which is not actually at the North Pole, but somewhere in the Arctic.

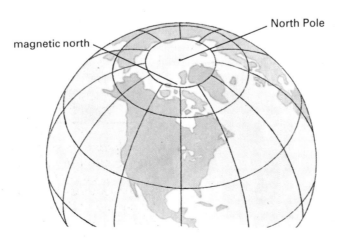

North Pole

magnetic north

The compasses used by hikers can be set to take account of this. With an orienteering compass like the one shown, when the arrow points along the magnetic north line*, then the four points of the compass are correctly as shown.*

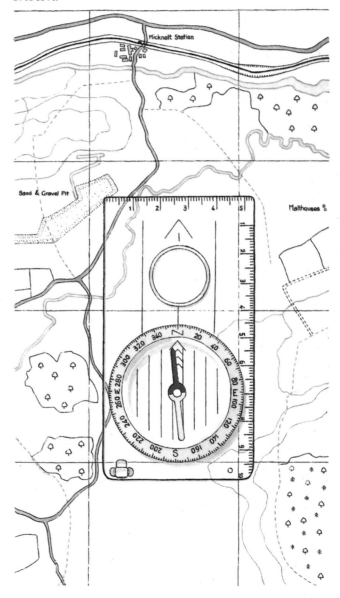

NES Arnold Ltd
Ludlow Hill Road
West Bridgford
Nottingham
NG2 6HD
Telephone: 0602 452204

Griffin & George Ltd
Bishops Meadow Road
Loughborough
Leicestershire, LE11 0RG
Telephone: 0509 233344

Philip Harris Ltd
Lynn Lane
Shenstone
Staffordshire, WS14 0EE
Telephone: 0543 480077

Berol Ltd
Oldmedow Road
Kings Lynn
Norfolk, PE30 4JR
Telephone: 0553 761211

RS Components
PO Box 427, 13-17 Epworth Street
London, EC2P 2HA
Telephone: 071-253-1222